GOREN'S BRIDGE QUIZZES

Charles Goren has played cards with princes and presidents, on footlockers in baseball dressing rooms, on airplanes crossing the Atlantic, on floodlit stages, and in more tournaments, gathering at one point more Master Points and championships than anyone else in the world. Other bridge players may accrue more points but it is unlikely that others will soon accrue a larger following. A popular teacher, he finds the combination of fifty-two cards and four players an endlessly fascinating subject, and travels across country and ocean as professional, lecturer, and TV personality. He is also a regular contributor to *Sports Illustrated,* and has a syndicated newspaper column and televised bridge show. Among his most recent books are *Goren's Bridge Complete,* a major revision of *the* standard handbook for all players, and, with Jack Olsen, *Bridge Is My Game.*

Goren's
Bridge Quizzes

CHARLES H. GOREN

DOLPHIN BOOKS

Doubleday & Company, Inc.
Garden City, New York
1966

The Dolphin Books edition is the first publication of
GOREN'S BRIDGE QUIZZES

Dolphin Books edition 1966

GOREN'S BRIDGE QUIZZES

FOREWORD

For many years I have stressed the importance of having fun when you play bridge. One way of achieving this end is by engaging in extended quizzes, and I trust that this book will be a step in that direction.

In the process of seeking innocent merriment we might just as well pause to pick up a few guides to winning procedure, and I have striven not to overlook the pedagogic features of my activities. You will observe that my philosophy does not stress the conventional (i.e., artificial angles of contract bridge) and if you follow your natural instincts you will have a good head start to a good score.

Frequent references are made to the point count, and I shall assume that you are familiar with it.

More for the record than anything else, the point count charts are listed below:

THE POINT COUNT TABLE (Table of High Cards)
Ace .... 4 points
King .... 3 points
Queen .... 2 points
Jack .... 1 point

The pack contains 40 points. An average hand contains 10 points.

Any honor other than an ace loses a point if it is unguarded or unprotected. If your hand contains four aces, you may add one point. If your hand has no aces, deduct one point.

Distributional Count (for purposes of opening the bidding)

                    Void .... 3 points
                    Singleton .... 2 points
                    Doubleton .... 1 point

If your hand contains a combined point count of 13 points, you have an optional opening bid. If you have 14 or more points, you have a mandatory opening bid.

DUMMY POINT COUNT TABLE

When you raise your partner with the intention of being the dummy, count your distributional points as follows:

                    A void is worth 5 points.
                    A singleton is worth 3 points.
                    A doubleton is worth 1 point.

If you raise your partner with a 4–3–3–3 distribution, deduct one point. Add one point to your hand for the possession of a fifth trump, and two points for each additional trump beyond five.

REQUIREMENTS FOR GAME

4 Spades or 4 Hearts 26 points in high cards between the combined hands and distribution, plus a fit in the major.

3 No Trump 26 points in high cards between the combined hands.

5 Clubs or 5 Diamonds 29 points in high cards and distribution between the combined hands.

Small slam—in a suit 33 points plus a fit.

Small slam at no trump 33 high-card points.

Grand slam in a suit 37 points plus a fit.

Grand slam at no trump 37 high-card points.

The point count is applied to opening suit bids.

The Blackwood Convention is employed on hands for which it is suitable, but if most readers use it here as frequently as they overdo it in actual play, their score will suffer. On hands where Blackwood is not apt to prove effective, the direct showing of specific aces is used on the way to many slams.

In these tests, ten points are awarded for each correct answer and, in cases where a particular alternate bid has merit, I have awarded a partial credit.

I'm not quite sure of what the passing grade should be. The quizzes vary in degree of difficulty and you will find it easier to score well in the early ones. If you score above 50 per cent in the last ten quizzes, you may look down your nose at a great many of your neighbors. If you do as well as 75 per cent, I'm sure I can get you a good partner for the next big tournament, and if you surpass that grade, you will either receive the adulation of your friends who will hail you as a Daniel come to judgment, or the contempt of your enemies who will be convinced that you have peeked at the answers. In any event it will provide a good contest.

Now, shake hands and come out fighting.

CHARLES H. GOREN

QUIZ 1

answers follow this quiz

1 As dealer you hold:
 ♠ x x x ♡ A 10 x x ◇ A K x ♣ x x x
 What is your opening bid? Your answer_____

2 As dealer you hold:
 ♠ Q J x ♡ K Q x ◇ A x x ♣ Q 10 x x
 What is your opening bid? Your answer_____

3 As dealer you hold:
 ♠ A J x x ♡ x x x ◇ A K Q x ♣ x x
 What is your opening bid? Your answer_____

4 Your partner opens with one spade. You hold:
 ♠ x x x x ♡ A x x ◇ x x x ♣ x x x
 What is your response? Your answer_____

5 Your partner opens with one spade. You hold:
 ♠ K J x x x ♡ K x x ◇ x x ♣ x x x
 What is your response? Your answer_____

6 Your partner opens with one spade. You hold:
 ♠ x x x ♡ K x x ◇ K Q x ♣ A Q x x
 What is your response? Your answer_____

7 As dealer you hold:
 ♠ J 10 x x ♡ A Q x ◇ A K x ♣ A Q x
 What is your opening bid? Your answer_____

8 Your partner opens with one no trump. You hold:
 ♠ A x x ♡ x x x ◇ A 10 x x x ♣ x x
 What is your response? Your answer_____

9 Your partner opens with one club. You hold:
 ♠ None ♡ K J x ◇ A Q 10 x x ♣ A x x x x
 What is your response? Your answer_____

10 As West you hold:

♠ A K x x x ♡ x x x ◊ Q x x ♣ J x

The bidding has proceeded:

SOUTH	WEST	NORTH	EAST
1 NT	Pass	2 NT	Pass
3 NT	Pass	Pass	Pass

What is your opening lead?   Your answer_____

ANSWERS

1 Pass. This hand contains but 11 points. You have no convenient rebid if partner responds with two clubs or two diamonds.

2 One Club. This hand contains 14 points and is therefore a mandatory opening bid. A rebid of one no trump is available over any response of one of a suit by partner.

3 One Spade. The suit below the doubleton. A one-diamond opening is improper. It affords no convenient rebid if partner responds with two clubs.

4 Pass. This hand contains 4 points and no distributional features, therefore there is no reason to keep the bidding alive.

5 Bid Two Spades. Do not get excited because of your fifth trump. The hand would be almost as good without it. Your hand contains only three and a half playing tricks, which is not at all impressive. Take half credit if you bid four spades. A bid of three spades is a distinct overbid and receives one demerit.

6 Two No Trump. This is an exact descriptive bid. Your hand has all the adverse suits protected and a point count of 14. Since you have an opening bid facing an opening bid, you should insist on game. A temporizing bid of two clubs does not have much to recommend it.

7 One Club. This hand has the proper pattern for a no-trump opening, but it is too strong for one no trump for which the top limit is 18 high-card points, and not strong enough for a two-no-trump opening, which requires 22 high-card points.

8 Two No Trump. You have a high-card point count of 8, sufficient to justify a raise even without the fifth diamond. It would be improper to bid two diamonds, which would deny the high-card count for a raise.

9 Two Diamonds. A jump-shift response suggesting slam possibilities. Your good trump fit and controls justify such optimism. You have 19 points in support of clubs.

10 A Small Spade. Do not make the mistake of leading the king. Partner may have only two spades, in which case he will be unable to return the suit when it is established. You should be willing to give up the first spade trick so that if your partner obtains the lead, he will have a spade left to return and the rest of the suit will probably run. Take only half credit if you led the king of spades.

*Your score*_____

1 As dealer you hold:
   ♠ K Q 10 x ♡ J x x ◇ A Q x ♣ A J x
   What is your opening bid?   Your answer_____

2 As dealer you hold:
   ♠ A 10 x ♡ Q x x ◇ K Q x ♣ A x x x
   What is your opening bid?   Your answer_____

3 As dealer you hold:
   ♠ A x x ♡ K x ◇ A K J x x ♣ Q x x
   What is your opening bid?   Your answer_____

4 Your partner opens with one heart. You hold:
   ♠ K J x ♡ J x x ◇ A Q x x ♣ A Q x
   What is your response?   Your answer_____

5 Your partner opens with one heart. You hold:
   ♠ x x ♡ K x x x ◇ K Q J x ♣ J 10 x
   What is your response?   Your answer_____

6 Your partner opens with one no trump. You hold:
   ♠ Q J x x x x ♡ x ◇ x ♣ Q x x x
   What is your response?   Your answer_____

7 Your partner opens with one heart. You hold:
   ♠ A J 10 x ♡ J x x x ◇ x x ♣ x x x
   What is your response?   Your answer_____

8 Your partner opens with two no trump. You hold:
   ♠ Q x x ♡ 10 x x x ◇ x x x ♣ x x x
   What is your response?   Your answer_____

9 As dealer you hold:
   ♠ Q 10 x x ♡ K 10 x x ◇ x ♣ A Q x x
   What is your opening bid?   Your answer_____

10 As West you hold:
    ♠ KQJx ♡ Ax ◇ Axxxx ♣ xx
    The bidding has proceeded:

    SOUTH   WEST   NORTH   EAST
    1 NT   Pass   2 NT   Pass
    3 NT   Pass   Pass   Pass
    What is your opening lead?   Your answer_____

ANSWERS

1 One No Trump. You have 17 points with three suits stopped and a balanced hand. Your one-no-trump opening describes the strength of your hand in a single bid.

2 One Club. This hand is not strong enough for a one-no-trump opening since it contains only 15 high-card points. Take only three points if you opened with one no trump.

3 One No Trump. The 5–3–3–2 distribution is acceptable, all suits are stopped, and you have 17 points. If you open with one diamond, you will be in a quandary if partner responds with one heart, for your hand will be a shade too weak for a rebid of two no trump, but too strong for a rebid of two diamonds or one no trump. Take only half credit if your answer was one diamond.

4 Three No Trump. You have the right distribution and high-card strength (17 points). A two-no-trump response would be highly improper, for it would place your hand with a maximum of 15 high-card points. A bid of two diamonds, though acceptable, will lead to complications when you jump to three no trump on your rebid. Partner will not have the precise picture of your hand that the three-no-trump take-out offers. Take only half credit if your bid was two diamonds.

5 Two Diamonds. An indirect bid is necessary because the hand is too good for a single raise and not good enough for a jump raise to three hearts. Hearts will be supported on the next round.

6 Four Spades. Game is reasonably certain, but slam is entirely out of the question. Such a pre-emptive response

describes a hand which is not rich in high cards. Give yourself a demerit if you bid but two spades.

7　Two Hearts—not one spade. You cannot afford to do both and you should make the more constructive bid, which is a raise of partner's major suit with adequate support. Take only half credit if you responded with one spade.

8　Pass. A point count of 2 does not justify a raise. An opening two-no-trump bid is not forcing. In the absence of distribution, a count of 4 points is required before a raise to game is made.

9　One Club. This hand contains a high-card point count of 11, but the distributional features, that is, the singleton, or if you prefer, the two side suits, account for an additional 2 points, bringing your total to 13—an optional opening bid. The option should be exercised because of the possession of eight cards in the major suits, and the ease of rebidding. Take only half credit if your answer was "Pass."

10　The King of Spades. While the diamonds are longer, the spades can be more readily established. Half credit is awarded to the lead of the fourth best diamond.

Your score＿＿＿＿＿

QUIZ 3

1 As dealer you hold:
   ♠ A x x   ♡ J x x x   ◇ A x x   ♣ A J x
   What is your opening bid?   Your answer_____

2 As dealer you hold:
   ♠ Q J x   ♡ A x x   ◇ K 10 x   ♣ Q J 10 x
   What is your opening bid?   Your answer_____

3 As dealer you hold:
   ♠ A Q x x x   ♡ A K x   ◇ A K x   ♣ x x
   What is your opening bid?   Your answer_____

4 Your partner opens with one club. You hold:
   ♠ A x x   ♡ K J x x   ◇ A x x x   ♣ x x
   What is your response?   Your answer_____

5 Your partner opens with one club. You hold:
   ♠ A K J x x x x x   ♡ A   ◇ Q J 10 x   ♣ None
   What is your response?   Your answer_____

6 Your partner opens with one club. You hold:
   ♠ K J x   ♡ K Q x   ◇ A 10 x x   ♣ A x x
   What is your response?   Your answer_____

7 As South you hold:
   ♠ K J x x x   ♡ A x   ◇ K x x   ♣ A x x
   The bidding has proceeded:

SOUTH	WEST	NORTH	EAST
1 ♠	Pass	2 ♠	Pass
?			

   What do you bid now?   Your answer_____

10

8   As South you hold:

♠ A x x ♥ A K x x x ♦ K Q x ♣ x x

The bidding has proceeded:

SOUTH	WEST	NORTH	EAST
1 ♥	Pass	2 ♥	Pass
?			

What do you bid now?   Your answer_____

9   As South you hold:

♠ K 10 x x ♥ A K J x x ♦ A K x ♣ x

The bidding has proceeded:

SOUTH	WEST	NORTH	EAST
1 ♥	Pass	1 ♠	Pass
?			

What do you bid now?   Your answer_____

10 As West you hold:

♠ Q J x x ♥ J 10 x ♦ K x x ♣ x x x

The bidding has proceeded:

SOUTH	WEST	NORTH	EAST
1 NT	Pass	2 NT	Pass
3 NT	Pass	Pass	Pass

What is your opening lead?   Your answer_____

ANSWERS

1   One Club. This hand contains 14 points and is, therefore, a mandatory opening bid. It is not strong enough, however, for a one-no-trump opening which requires from 16 to 18 high-card points. This is an example of an opening bid on a three-card minor suit when no other satisfactory bid is available. Your rebid will be convenient. If partner calls one heart, you will raise. If he bids one of any other suit, you rebid one no trump.

2   One Club. This hand contains 13 points which would make it an optional opening bid, but the presence of two tens should convert it into a mandatory opening bid. Rebid one no trump over any response from partner at the level of one. Take only half credit if you passed.

3 One Spade. Take no credit at all if your answer was two spades because of your 20 high-card points in aces, kings, and one queen. Admittedly you have a splendid hand, but your count amounts to only 21 points. The requirements for a demand two-opening call is 25 points with a five-card suit. Remember, when you open with a demand bid, partner is obliged to carry on to game with possibly no values in his hand. Since you need about 6 points to make a game, you may rely on partner to do his part if he is so endowed.

4 One Heart. This hand contains only 12 points, and is, therefore, fractionally short of the high-card requirements for a two-no-trump response. It is preferable to show the major suit first and then try no trump later. A response of one diamond would also be acceptable. Take only half credit if your response was two no trump.

5 Two Spades. A jump shift, suggesting a slam. Support for partner's suit is not a prerequisite for a jump-shift response if your suit is self-sustaining. A one-spade response receives half credit only.

6 Three No Trump. You have a balanced hand with a point count of 17—three no trump is an exact descriptive bid, which is preferable to the temporizing call of one diamond. Partner will know you have a 4–3–3–3 distribution plus a point count range of from 16 to 18.

7 Pass. You have 16 points when you re-evaluate your fifth spade for being supported, but partner needs exactly 10 points for your side to have the required 26. If you bid three spades, he may go to game on a good 8 or 9 points, and your prospects for making the game appear dim. Take half credit if you bid three spades.

8 Three Hearts. You have 18 points now that partner has raised you (add one point for the fifth trump) and need but a trifle more than a minimum raise from partner to reach the game zone. He will oblige you if his hand warrants a game bid.

9 Three Diamonds. A jump shift, forcing to game. There are distinct chances for a slam and even a jump to four

spades over one would not do full justice to this hand. When you subsequently raise spades, partner will place you with at most one club since you have bid two suits and jumped in the third, and he therefore will be in a position to aim at a slam if there is no duplication of values. Take only half credit if your bid was four spades.

10 The jack of hearts is the preferred lead with a small spade as a second choice. The spade lead might sacrifice a trick. The heart lead is not apt to do so.

*Your score*_____

1 You are vulnerable. Your non-vulnerable opponent opens
   with one club and you hold:
   ♠ x   ♡ A J 10 x x   ◇ A K x x   ♣ x x x
   What do you bid?   Your answer_____

2 As South you hold:
   ♠ A 10 x   ♡ A K Q 10 x   ◇ x x x   ♣ K x
   The bidding has proceeded:

SOUTH	WEST	NORTH	EAST
1 ♡	Pass	2 ♣	Pass
?			

   What do you bid now?   Your answer_____

3 As South you hold:
   ♠ J x   ♡ 10 x x   ◇ A K x x x   ♣ Q 10 x
   The bidding has proceeded as follows:

NORTH	EAST	SOUTH	WEST
1 ♣	Pass	1 ◇	Pass
1 NT	Pass	?	

   What do you bid now?   Your answer_____

4 As South you hold:
   ♠ 10 x   ♡ A x x x   ◇ K J x x   ♣ K 10 x
   The bidding has proceeded:

NORTH	EAST	SOUTH	WEST
1 ♠	Double	?	

   What do you bid?   Your answer_____

5 As South you hold:
   ♠ A K 10 x   ♡ A J   ◇ K Q J x x x   ♣ x
   The bidding has proceeded:

SOUTH	WEST	NORTH	EAST
1 ◇	Pass	1 ♡	2 ♣
2 ♠	Pass	3 ♡	Pass
?			

   What do you bid now?   Your answer_____

6   As South you hold:
    ♠ Q 7   ♡ A K x x x   ◇ K Q x x   ♣ A K
    The bidding has proceeded:

SOUTH	WEST	NORTH	EAST
1 ♡	Pass	1 ♠	Pass
3 ◇	Pass	3 NT	Pass
?			

    What do you bid now?   Your answer_____

7   Partner opens with one spade. You hold:
    ♠ x x   ♡ K Q x x x   ◇ K x x   ♣ 10 x x
    What is your response?   Your answer_____

8   As South you hold:
    ♠ x x   ♡ x x   ◇ J 10 9 x x x   ♣ K x x
    The bidding has proceeded:

NORTH	EAST	SOUTH	WEST
1 ♠	2 ◇	?	

    What do you bid?   Your answer_____

9   As South you hold:
    ♠ K x x x x   ♡ K Q x x   ◇ None   ♣ K Q 10 x
    The bidding has proceeded:

NORTH	EAST	SOUTH	WEST
1 ♠	Pass	3 ♠	Pass
4 ♣	Pass	5 ♣	Pass
5 ♡	Pass	?	

    What do you bid now?   Your answer_____

10 As West you hold:
    ♠ J 10 9 x   ♡ J x x x x   ◇ K   ♣ Q x x
    The bidding has proceeded:

NORTH	EAST	SOUTH	WEST
1 ♣	Pass	1 ♠	Pass
2 ♡	Pass	2 NT	Pass
3 NT	Pass	Pass	Pass

    What is your opening lead?   Your answer_____

15

ANSWERS

1 One Heart. While you have the honor strength to justify a double, such procedure is not advisable since partner will probably respond with one spade, which would make it necessary to bid two hearts. And since your suit is not very strong, such a bid runs the risk of a sizable penalty.

2 In view of the promoted value of the king of clubs, your hand has a trick-taking potentiality of seven, which with the excess high-card values justifies a jump rebid, and the recommended call is three hearts.

3 Two No Trump. You have slightly better than an average hand in high cards and, if partner's opening bid is not an absolute minimum, there may be a chance for game. This hand is actually somewhat better than it counts by reason of the promoted value of the queen of clubs. If partner's hand is near minimum, he will pass. Take 5 points if you elected to pass.

4 Redouble. Your hand is slightly above average in high-card strength (11 points). When partner's opening bid has been doubled, the possessor of an above-average hand should designate it by a routine redouble. Trump support for partner is not necessary in this situation. In point of fact the redouble may be made with slightly less high-card strength when support for partner is held. A bid of one no trump over the double is given a demerit.

5 Partner may not have much honor strength, but he ought to have great length in hearts, which is enough for your purposes. A raise to four hearts is therefore recommended. Nothing is to be gained by rebidding the diamonds. Partner may be unable to carry on.

6 Pass. You have had your say and the time has come to relax. Any further conversation by you would be just filibuster. On the basis of a mere one-over-one response, you have insisted upon a game and partner has shown no animation. For a mathematical demonstration let us point out that North may have as little as 6 points (sometimes

16

even a little less), and you have but 21 with no fit established. You are therefore not in slam territory.

7   One No Trump. With this evenly balanced hand we are not inclined to make any bid which would force partner to speak again at an increased level; we therefore veto a response of two hearts and vote in favor of a one-no-trump bid. This hand contains only 8 points which makes it well within the limits of a one-no-trump response. Normally it takes 10 points to justify taking out at the level of two unless a highly unbalanced hand is held.

8   Discretion calls for a pass. If there were any assurance that this would prove to be the final contract, a vociferous double would be in order. But it is highly unlikely that the two-diamond bid will stand. It is reasonable to expect that there will be a rescue bid and there is grave danger that partner, relying upon you for certain high-card values because of your double, will take some step that will be distasteful to you, such as doubling the rescue bid, toward the defeat of which you will be able to contribute little or nothing.

9   Seven Spades. On the basis of your partner's strong bidding there can be little doubt that the trump suit is solid. It will be observed that North bypassed an easy chance to show the ace of diamonds, so it may be assumed that he does not have that card. This makes it all the more convincing that there is no trump loser. So that a grand-slam bid in spades is quite in order.

10 The Jack of Spades. Even though you are leading right up to the bidder, the complete sequence makes this perfectly safe. It is better to lead a complete sequence up to the declarer's strength. Leading dummy's suit when you have a broken holding of this sort is not frequently profitable. The lead of a low club has some merit if it uncovers some length in partner's hand and for that reason is awarded five points.

*Your score*_____

QUIZ 5

1 As South you hold:
♠ K x x　♡ K x x　◊ A x x　♣ K 10 x x
The bidding has proceeded:

SOUTH	WEST	NORTH	EAST
1 ♣	Pass	1 ♠	Pass
1 NT	Pass	2 ♣	Pass
?			

What do you bid now?　　　Your answer———

2 As South you hold:
♠ A K x x x　♡ x x　◊ A Q 10 x　♣ x x
The bidding has proceeded:

SOUTH	WEST	NORTH	EAST
1 ♠	Pass	2 ♡	Pass
?			

What do you bid now?　　　Your answer———

3 As South you hold:
♠ A J x x　♡ A Q 10 x　◊ Q J 10 x　♣ x
The bidding has proceeded:

EAST	SOUTH	WEST	NORTH
1 ♣	Double	Pass	1 ♡
2 ♣	?		

What do you bid now?　　　Your answer———

4 As South you hold:
♠ K J x x　♡ A 10　◊ J x x　♣ A K J x
The bidding has proceeded:

NORTH	EAST	SOUTH	WEST
Pass	1 ♡	Double	Pass
2 ◊	Pass	?	

What do you bid now?　　　Your answer———

5 You are South, have 60 part score, and hold:
♠ KJ10x ♡ Axx ◇ xx ♣ AJxx
The bidding has proceeded:

SOUTH	WEST	NORTH	EAST
1 ♣	Pass	1 ♠	Pass
2 ♠	Pass	3 ◇	Pass
?			

What do you bid now?   Your answer_____

6 As South you hold:
♠ Axx ♡ AQx ◇ AKxxx ♣ Ax
The bidding has proceeded:

SOUTH	WEST	NORTH	EAST
1 ◇	Pass	2 ♣	Pass
3 NT	Pass	5 ◇	Pass
?			

What do you bid now?   Your answer_____

7 As South you hold:
♠ Ax ♡ A10x ◇ QJx ♣ QJxxx
The bidding has proceeded:

NORTH	EAST	SOUTH	WEST
1 ◇	Pass	2 ♣	Pass
3 ♣	Pass	?	

What do you bid now?   Your answer_____

8 Both sides have 60 part score. You are South and hold:
♠ KJ10xx ♡ AKxxx ◇ None ♣ 10xx
The bidding has proceeded:

EAST	SOUTH	WEST	NORTH
1 ◇	?		

What do you bid?   Your answer_____

9 As South you hold:
♠ Qx ♡ AKxxx ◇ xxx ♣ AJx
The bidding has proceeded:

NORTH	EAST	SOUTH	WEST
1 ♠	Pass	2 ♡	Pass
3 ♡	Pass	?	

What do you bid now?   Your answer_____

10   You are West and hold:
     ♠ 8 2   ♡ 7 6 4   ◇ Q 7 3   ♣ A J 9 5 2
     The bidding has proceeded:

SOUTH	WEST	NORTH	EAST
2 NT	Pass	4 NT	Pass
6 NT	Pass	Pass	Pass

     What is your opening lead?   Your answer_____

ANSWERS

1   Pass. There is a temptation to return to two spades on
    this hand, but it should be curbed. Your hand is such a
    minimum that there can be no reasonable question of a
    game. Partner may have only four weak spades, but
    surely he has at least four clubs, which would make the
    latter contract safer. A bid of two spades might encour-
    age partner to bid more.

2   Two Spades. Despite the fact that you have more than a
    minimum, no other satisfactory rebid is available. The
    hand is not strong enough to rebid at the level of three.

3   Two Hearts. While this appears to be a strong hand, you
    must not lose sight of the fact that you forced partner to
    bid and he may have nothing. A raise to three hearts
    would be improper because as far as you know it would
    not be safe. If partner has any definite values he will bid
    again after your single raise. If he does, you may then
    contract for game.

4   Pass. There is no reason to foresee game possibilities and
    there is no action you can take at this point that is not
    fraught with danger. Partner has been brought into the
    battle perhaps much against his will, and he may have
    little or nothing. A bid of two spades would be bad tactics
    and a call of two no trump would be the act of a man
    who looks upon currency with complete disdain.

5   Three Hearts. This bid can be construed by partner in no
    other light than that of an ace-showing bid. Spades have
    been agreed upon as trumps and partner, by overbidding

the game, is not merely showing that he has diamonds, which actually he may not have, but is making a distinct effort toward slam. You have the right kind of cards for slam purposes and you should not be bashful about mentioning the fact. From here in you must let partner do all the heavy work, inasmuch as you will then have told the whole story. Take half credit if your bid was four spades, which, while not the best bid available, is a step in the right direction.

6 Seven Diamonds. You will probably claim the hand after the opening lead. Partner naturally has fine diamond support, a good club suit, a singleton, and a king. Else how could he combine a two club take-out with a jump to five diamonds? Take only three points if you bid six diamonds or six no trump.

7 Three Spades. When the promoted value of the diamond holding is taken into consideration, your hand is better than an opening bid. Partner has shown that he, too, has better than an opening bid because of his raise at the level of three so that slam possibilities may be visualized. The suggested call is three spades—an ace-showing bid with the intention of showing the ace of hearts on the next round. This should leave it up to partner to decide the fate of the hand. A bid of three no trump over partner's three-club bid would be grossly inadequate.

8 One Spade. Since a fight may be anticipated, you should arrange to mention both suits if it becomes expedient to do so, and the proper way to plan this is by a mere overcall of one spade. Something is bound to happen around the table on the first round and you should have a chance to mention the heart suit at a reasonable level. No credit is awarded to a double or an overcall of one heart.

9 Four Clubs. You should be very much alert to the possibilities of a slam. You have more than an opening bid and partner presumably has at least a trick more than an opening bid, in view of the fact that he raised you to the three level. The proper procedure is to bid four clubs. If

partner fails to co-operate, then nothing has been lost and you may quit at four hearts.

10 A Heart. Generally the seven is selected, but for deceptive purposes, sometimes the lead of the four may bring good results. It is doubtful whether it will matter much to partner. On this particular bidding he can hardly have any strength. Under no circumstances should a club be led. Against the slam contract you have an excellent chance, particularly if the declarer misguesses the location of the queen of diamonds. Don't make any lead that might sacrifice a trick. Aggressive action is usually not advisable against no-trump slams. It is better to protect your holdings. The lead of the eight of spades may work out well and is awarded five points.

*Your score*_____

1 Partner opens with one heart and you hold:
♠ A K x   ♡ x x x   ◇ K x x   ♣ A K x x
What is your response?   Your answer_____

2 As South you hold:
♠ K x x   ♡ A 10 x x x   ◇ x x x   ♣ Q x
The bidding has proceeded:

SOUTH	WEST	NORTH	EAST
Pass	Pass	1 ♡	1 ♠
?			

What do you bid now?   Your answer_____

3 As South you hold:
♠ x   ♡ A Q J x x   ◇ x x   ♣ K Q 10 x x
The bidding has proceeded:

SOUTH	WEST	NORTH	EAST
1 ♡	Pass	2 ◇	Pass
?			

What do you bid now?   Your answer_____

4 You are South, opponents are vulnerable, and you hold:
♠ x   ♡ A J x x   ◇ A J x x   ♣ K Q 10 x
The bidding has proceeded:

NORTH	EAST	SOUTH	WEST
1 ♠	Double	?	

What do you bid?   Your answer_____

5 As South you hold:
♠ x x   ♡ K J 10 x x x   ◇ A 10   ♣ K x x
The bidding has proceeded:

NORTH	EAST	SOUTH	WEST
1 ♠	Pass	2 ♡	Pass
2 ♠	Pass	?	

What do you bid now?   Your answer_____

23

6 As South you hold:
♠ 10 x ♡ J x x x ◇ A J x x ♣ A 10 x
The bidding has proceeded:

NORTH EAST SOUTH WEST
4 ♡ 4 ♠ ?

What do you bid? Your answer_____

7 As South you hold:
♠ x x ♡ x x x ◇ A x x x ♣ Q J 10 x
The bidding has proceeded:

NORTH EAST SOUTH WEST
1 ♡ 1 ♠ Pass 2 ♠
2 NT Pass ?

What do you bid now? Your answer_____

8 Both sides are vulnerable. You are South and hold:
♠ x ♡ x x x ◇ A K J x x ♣ Q x x
The bidding has proceeded:

NORTH EAST SOUTH WEST
1 ♠ 2 ♡ ?

What do you bid? Your answer_____

9 You are South and vulnerable (opponents are not). You hold:
♠ 10 ♡ x x x ◇ A K x x x ♣ K Q 10 x
The bidding has proceeded:

WEST NORTH EAST SOUTH
3 ♡ 4 ♠ Pass ?

What do you bid? Your answer_____

10 You are West and hold:
♠ Q x ♡ x x ◇ K J 10 x x ♣ Q J 10 x
The bidding has proceeded:

SOUTH WEST NORTH EAST
1 NT Pass 2 NT Pass
3 NT Pass Pass Pass

What is your opening lead? Your answer_____

ANSWERS

1 Three No Trump. Despite the fact that you have four and a half honor tricks, a slam cannot be contemplated without some approval from partner. Your bid announced a balanced holding with 16 to 18 high-card points. If partner makes a mild slam try, you are, of course, quite agreeable. On the other hand, if partner passes, you should not feel any loss, for a slam will have a remote chance at best.

2 Two Hearts. Any excitement induced by possession of the fifth heart is not justified. This is not a very good hand. What would your attitude be, for example, if the three of hearts were a little diamond? The fifth heart doesn't add too much to the cause. Take only half credit if your bid was four hearts.

3 Two Hearts. At these prices you cannot afford to show the club suit. Your hand is not strong enough to support a rebid at the level of three. If partner proceeds in the face of your two-heart rebid, you will have time enough to speak of clubs. Charge yourself one demerit if your bid was three clubs.

4 Redouble. There is no second choice even remotely in sight. East would have done better to stay home and it is your duty to set the stage for the ensuing bloodshed. What, you query, if partner is left in to play at one spade redoubled? The answer is that it just won't happen, because either East or West will see to it that it doesn't. If they should decide to leave him in, sit back and relax; partner won't have any trouble taking seven tricks, which will yield a game. The redouble requests partner to hold his tongue for one round, permitting you to take charge. It is your intention, of course, to start operations on any bid made by either East or West.

5 Two No Trump. I am not inclined to be disdainful of a good six-card major suit, but on the other hand, no other bid is suitable. A rebid of hearts would suggest that the

25

merit of the hand lies merely in that suit, and if partner is unable to support it he might very well give up. A rebid of two no trump, while it does not describe the heart suit, does greater justice to the hand as a whole and is more apt to encourage partner to proceed.

6   Five Hearts. Not so much because you think you can make it, which actually is somewhat doubtful, but because you should have reason to believe that there is little hope of defeating four spades. Partner has announced a hand with little if any defensive strength, and you may not be able to cash even one heart trick. Take only half credit if you passed.

7   Three No Trump. You have a good substantial 7 points and have not yet made your presence felt. Even if partner is stretching a point, you should have a reasonable play for game. After all, partner has contracted for eight tricks against two bidding opponents with a passing partner, and should welcome your contribution to the general welfare.

8   Despite the fact that you hold an average hand in high cards, which is normally reason to be enthusiastic when partner opens the bidding, there is no bid that you can safely make at this point. If you choose to bid three diamonds, partner is forced to speak again. In all likelihood, his rebid will be three spades, which, of course, you will be obliged to pass, leaving your partner in a very doubtful contract. You have no real choice, therefore, but to pass and await developments. The only conceivable alternative is to make a penalty double of two hearts which is somewhat too venturesome to suit the tastes of this department. Take five points for a double.

9   The lack of trump support should be no deterrent to appropriate action on your part. Partner has made it clear that his spade suit is self-sustaining. On a basis of simple arithmetic, slam prospects are bright. Partner should be able to win nine of the ten tricks for which he has contracted, and you can win at least three. The opposition has made scientific investigation impossible, and we are

inclined to give vent to our sporting instinct. We are in favor of a bid of six spades or at least five. We would not consider a pass. A call of five diamonds is pointless and can only be of assistance to the enemy in the selection of an opening lead. Take eight points if you bid five spades.

10 The Queen of Clubs. Here again the preference is given to the more solid suit, rather than to the longer one. A diamond lead might very well be into the declarer's ace-queen. Take half credit for the lead of a diamond.

*Your score*_____

1 Partner opens with one spade. You hold:
   ♠ J x   ♡ A x x   ◇ A x x x   ♣ J x x x
   What is your response?   Your answer_____

2 You open with one club. Partner responds one no trump.
   You hold:
   ♠ A K x x   ♡ x x   ◇ x x x   ♣ A K x x
   What do you bid now?   Your answer_____

3 Partner opens with three no trump and you hold:
   ♠ J 10 x x x x x   ♡ K   ◇ K   ♣ K Q x x
   What is your response?   Your answer_____

4 As South you hold:
   ♠ K Q x x   ♡ A x x   ◇ Q x x   ♣ x x x
   The bidding has proceeded:

NORTH	EAST	SOUTH	WEST
1 ♡	2 ♣	?	

   What do you bid?   Your answer_____

5 As South you hold:
   ♠ Q J x x   ♡ K Q J x x   ◇ A Q x   ♣ x
   The bidding has proceeded:

SOUTH	WEST	NORTH	EAST
1 ♡	Pass	2 ♡	Pass
?			

   What do you bid now?   Your answer_____

6 As South you hold:
   ♠ x x   ♡ x x   ◇ A Q x x   ♣ A Q x x x
   The bidding has proceeded:

WEST	NORTH	EAST	SOUTH
1 ♡	Pass	2 ♡	Pass
Pass	2 ♠	Pass	?

   What do you bid now?   Your answer_____

7   As South you hold:
    ♠ Q x x   ♡ A Q x x x   ◇ J 10 x x   ♣ x
    The bidding has proceeded:
    WEST   NORTH   EAST   SOUTH
    1 ◇   2 ♣   Pass   ?
    What do you bid now?   Your answer_____

8   As South you hold:
    ♠ K x   ♡ None   ◇ K x x x x x   ♣ A K x x x
    The bidding has proceeded:
    SOUTH   WEST   NORTH   EAST
    1 ◇   Double 2 ♣   2 ♡
    ?
    What do you bid now?   Your answer_____

9   As South you hold:
    ♠ A K   ♡ K 10 x x x   ◇ A x x x   ♣ Q x
    The bidding has proceeded:
    SOUTH   WEST   NORTH   EAST
    1 ♡   2 ♣   Pass   Pass
    ?
    What do you bid now?   Your answer_____

10 You are West and hold:
    ♠ x   ♡ x x x x   ◇ K Q J x x   ♣ 10 x x
    The bidding has proceeded:
    NORTH   EAST   SOUTH   WEST
    1 ♡   1 ♠   1 NT   Pass
    2 NT   Pass   3 NT   Pass
    Pass   Double Pass   Pass
    Pass
    What is your opening lead?   Your answer_____

ANSWERS

1   The proper response on this hand is one no trump. De-
    spite the fact that you have two aces, no other response
    is acceptable. To be sure, this is a maximum containing
    10 points, the textbook limit. If partner rebids, you may

decide to take further action. If he should pass, you will find it highly unlikely that you would have missed a game.

2 Pass. Game is rather remote. Your hand contains but 14 points and partner cannot have as many as 12, else he would not have responded with one no trump. It is true that partner's response of one no trump to a bid of one club is apt to be somewhat better than the average one-no-trump response, but it could not possibly approach 12 points. A rebid of two spades risks having partner return to three clubs, for which you are not fully prepared.

3 Seven No Trump. Partner is marked with all the aces. Figure it out. He could not have 25 points (a minimum three-no-trump bid) without having all the aces. You have a count of 12 which insures the partnership of 37 points. Since the opponents are limited to 3, they cannot hold an ace. There is a remote possibility that partner may be lacking the king of spades, but this risk is worth assuming. Moreover, you will almost surely make thirteen tricks without the king of spades.

4 Two Hearts. The fact that you are making a free bid will show that you have a good hand. Don't make the mistake of bidding two spades. Such a bid will almost automatically land you in game. Figure it out. If partner rebids three hearts, under compulsion you will surely take him to four without any idea of whether or not he has more than a minimum.

5 Three Hearts. While it is true that partner's response was not of the encouraging variety and that you have not much in the way of excess strength, nevertheless, this hand has distinct game-going possibilities if partner's values happen to fit well. This hand is rich in playing tricks, having more than six and a half winners, which warrants taking one more step. To put it another way, if partner has the equivalent of an ace and a king, you should have an easy game. Take eight points if your bid was two spades, which is another way of inviting a game.

6 Pass. This may appear to be a symptom indicating that

my blood is thinning out, but actually I feel that it is a sign of good business sense. You can hardly hope for game. Partner obviously has no aspirations. He simply doesn't want to let the opposition run off with a bargain. If it were his purpose to go places, he would have acted immediately over the opening bid of one heart, at which point it would have been a very simple matter to have overcalled with one spade. A demerit is assessed for bidding over two spades.

7 Pass. There can be no bright prospect for game when partner fails to make a take-out double. It is extremely dangerous to experiment with a suit that is higher in rank than partner's suit. If he does not like hearts, he may have to return to three clubs and then the fur might start flying.

8 Five Clubs. It is true that partner has not advertised a strong hand, since he failed to redouble, and there is some doubt as to whether you can make it, but it looks very much as though the enemy are about to bid four hearts which, apparently, you have no hope of defeating. Since you will feel constrained to make a sacrifice bid in that event, you might as well do it first as last and put the pressure of guessing right squarely up to West.

9 Double. This will indicate a strong opening and gives partner several choices. He may bid diamonds, spades, return to hearts, or if he feels so inclined he may leave the double in. From your standpoint, that should not be hard to take.

10 The Spade. While the king of diamonds is an inviting lead, nevertheless, with a sound partner, it is mandatory to lead the spade. It is conventional that when partner bids a suit and then doubles the opponents' no-trump contract, he demands unconditionally that you lead his suit. On the actual hand, the lead of the king of diamonds permitted declarer to fulfill the contract.

*Your score*____

QUIZ 8

1   You open with one heart. Partner responds with one no trump. You hold:
     ♠ x x   ♡ A K x x   ◇ A Q x x   ♣ J x x
     What do you bid now?   Your answer_____

2   As dealer you hold the following hand:
     ♠ A K x   ♡ K Q 10   ◇ Q 10 x   ♣ A 10 x x
     What is your opening bid?   Your answer_____

3   As dealer you hold:
     ♠ A K Q x   ♡ x x   ◇ A K J x   ♣ A Q x
     What is your opening bid?   Your answer_____

4   As South you hold:
     ♠ K Q x x   ♡ x   ◇ A K J x   ♣ A 10 x x
     The bidding has proceeded:

SOUTH	WEST	NORTH	EAST
1 ◇	Pass	1 ♡	Pass
1 ♠	Pass	2 NT	Pass
?			

     What do you bid now?   Your answer_____

5   As South you hold:
     ♠ A J x x   ♡ x x   ◇ x x x   ♣ K 10 x x
     The bidding has proceeded:

NORTH	EAST	SOUTH	WEST
1 ◇	1 ♡	1 ♠	2 ♡
3 ♠	4 ♡	?	

     What do you bid now?   Your answer_____

6 As South you hold:
  ♠ J 10 x x ♡ A Q J x x ◇ K x x ♣ x
  The bidding has proceeded:

NORTH	EAST	SOUTH	WEST
1 ♠	Pass	2 ♡	Pass
3 ♠	Pass	?	

  What do you bid now?   Your answer_____

7 As South you hold:
  ♠ Q J x x ♡ A K Q ◇ A K x x ♣ x x
  The bidding has proceeded:

SOUTH	WEST	NORTH	EAST
1 ◇	Pass	1 ♠	Pass
?			

  What do you bid now?   Your answer_____

8 As South you hold:
  ♠ Q x x x ♡ x ◇ A x x ♣ A K x x x
  The bidding has proceeded:

NORTH	EAST	SOUTH	WEST
1 NT	Pass	3 ♣	Pass
3 ♠	Pass	?	

  What do you bid now?   Your answer_____

9 As South you hold:
  ♠ A J x x ♡ Q 10 x x ◇ x ♣ A K Q J
  The bidding has proceeded:

EAST	SOUTH	WEST	NORTH
1 ◇	Double	Pass	2 ♠
Pass	4 ♠	Pass	5 ♡
Pass	?		

  What do you bid now?   Your answer_____

10 You are West. You hold:
  ♠ Q J 10 ♡ Q 10 x x ◇ Q J 10 9 x ♣ x
  The bidding has proceeded:

SOUTH	WEST	NORTH	EAST
1 ♠	Pass	2 ◇	3 ♣
3 NT	Pass	Pass	Pass

  What is your opening lead?   Your answer_____

ANSWERS

1 Pass. Game appears to be hopeless and your hand is of the no-trump family. You will do well enough to take seven tricks without trying for eight.

2 One Club. This hand contains the proper distribution for one-no-trump opening, but it is a shade too strong. The maximum for a one-no-trump bid is 18 points. This hand possesses three tens above the limit of 18 and should be opened with one club. If partner responds with one of a suit a jump to two no trump is the suggested rebid.

3 One Diamond. You must not make the mistake of opening this hand with a two-no-trump bid because it has 23 high-card points. While you have the count for such a call, you do not have the heart suit guarded. Also, do not make the mistake of opening with one spade, because partner might find it difficult to respond. A one-diamond bid will allow partner to make a weak one-over-one response in hearts if he happens to have them. After that you may head for game.

4 Three Clubs. There can be no harm in giving a complete description of your hand at this point. If partner's values are in just the right places, there may be a slam, and if not, there is still time to play the hand at three no trump.

5 Pass. Your partner's jump to three spades after your free bid has committed your partnership to an ultimate game contract. However, it is not necessary for you to speak at this time when partner will have an opportunity to act on the same round of bidding. Your hand just about contains a minimum on which a free bid of one spade should have been made; if you make another free bid, partner will be justified in counting on you for additional values. There is a further consideration that partner may have a very lucrative double of four hearts, from which you should not bar him. When the bidding gets around to

North, he is obliged to do one of two things—either contract for four spades or double four hearts. He is entitled to that choice.

6 Five Spades. Considering the importance of your singleton club, your hand is the equivalent of an opening bid. Since partner has opened and jumped, there is a definite slam aroma about the hand, and your bid of five spades will convey that message.

7 Four Spades. There can be no question in your mind that a game in spades is odds-on to make. If partner had responded with five spades to a king and nothing else, he will need but to ruff a third club in your hand to total up ten tricks. A jump-shift rebid in hearts will ultimately lead to the same final bid, but would convey the impression that you had a singleton or a void in clubs when you finally bid four spades. Therefore, it is not recommended as a good choice of bids.

8 There is little doubt that slam prospects are now bright and a temporary bid should be made at this point. The suggested call is four diamonds, awaiting partner's next move. On the next round a jump should be made in spades. While on a basis of point count you have only 13, which should make the no-trump slam rather doubtful, the singleton heart in conjunction with four spades improves the hand's trick-taking power by virtually two tricks, and even a grand slam may be attainable if the hands fit perfectly. Take only half credit if your bid was six spades. This call, while it may be the winning one, gives partner no option.

9 Six Spades. The key to the situation is the singleton diamond. If partner has six spades to the king and the ace of hearts, twelve tricks can be counted. If he has a five-card spade suit, then surely he must have both heart honors to justify a jump and a bid beyond game.

10 The Queen of Diamonds. It is not very often that the lead of partner's suit should be ignored in favor of leading the opponents' suit, but this is one of the cases. The diamonds are so solid that two leads will probably establish the suit

for you. With one sure entry in spades and a probable one in hearts, this is the indicated procedure. It is extremely unlikely that your partner will have sufficient entries to bring in his club suit. You can almost surely defeat the contract yourself, and, as a matter of fact, the final bid might well have been doubled by you.

*Your score*_____

1 As South you hold:
♠ x x x ♡ None ◇ K J 10 x x x x ♣ x x x
The bidding has proceeded:

WEST NORTH EAST SOUTH
1 ♠   2 ♡   Pass ?

What do you bid? Your answer_____

2 Partner opens with one spade. You hold:
♠ x ♡ Q x x ◇ Q x x x ♣ J x x x x
What do you bid? Your answer_____

3 As South you hold:
♠ A K Q 10 x ♡ A K J x ◇ Q J x ♣ x
The bidding has proceeded:

SOUTH WEST NORTH EAST
1 ♠   Pass 1 NT Pass
?

What do you bid now? Your answer_____

4 Partner opens with one club and you hold:
♠ Q x x x ♡ J x x x ◇ Q 10 x x ♣ x
What is your response? Your answer_____

5 Both sides are vulnerable. As South you hold:
♠ Q x ♡ A Q x x x ◇ J 10 x ♣ x x x
The bidding has proceeded:

NORTH EAST SOUTH WEST
Pass   Pass Pass   1 ◇
1 ♠   2 ♣   ?

What do you bid now? Your answer_____

6 As South you hold:
♠ A K x x ♡ K Q 10 x ◇ x ♣ K x x x
The bidding has proceeded:

SOUTH	WEST	NORTH	EAST
1 ♠	2 ◇	Pass	Pass
?			

What do you bid now?   Your answer_____

7 Both sides are vulnerable. As South you hold:
♠ A ♡ K x ◇ A K Q J x x x ♣ A x x
The bidding has proceeded:

NORTH	EAST	SOUTH	WEST
Pass	1 ♠	?	

What do you bid?   Your answer_____

8 As South you hold:
♠ A K J x x ♡ Q x ◇ A x x ♣ A x x
The bidding has proceeded:

NORTH	EAST	SOUTH	WEST
1 ♡	Pass	1 ♠	Pass
3 ♠	Pass	?	

What do you bid now?   Your answer_____

9 As South you hold:
♠ A J x x x ♡ A x x ◇ K x x ♣ A Q
The bidding has proceeded:

SOUTH	WEST	NORTH	EAST
1 ♠	Pass	2 NT	3 ♣
?			

What do you bid now?   Your answer_____

10 As West you hold:
♠ K Q x ♡ J 10 9 x x ◇ 10 x x ♣ J x
The bidding has proceeded:

SOUTH	WEST	NORTH	EAST
1 ♠	Pass	2 ◇	3 ♣
3 NT	Pass	Pass	Pass

What is your opening lead?   Your answer_____

ANSWERS

1 Pass. The ice is very thin and you had better not move. It would be very pleasant to bid three diamonds, if you were sure your partner would not take any further action, but that would be wishful thinking. He is almost sure to bid again and probably more hearts. Your best bet is to pass and hope the opening bidder will take partner out of his misery by taking some action. It does not pay to rescue a partner who has not been doubled.

2 Pass. While there is a temptation to keep the bidding open in the hope that partner might have a second suit to show, it is not worth the risk with so few values. This is just one of those hands that you have to give up. Besides, you lack the 6 points which the textbook requires for a response to one no trump—this hand contains only 5 points.

3 Inasmuch as partner had sufficient values to keep the bidding open, at least 6 points, I would insist upon a game contract. The recommended bid is three hearts, a jump shift which is forcing to game. If partner returns to three spades, bid four. If partner has four little hearts, that should be the best contract; if he returns to three no trump, you have sufficient values to make that contract odds-on. Take half credit if your bid was three no trump. No credit is awarded to a bid of three spades.

4 One Diamond. Even though the hand does not contain 6 points in high cards, we dislike to pass partner out in a club bid where there is any reasonable excuse for bidding. Partner may have a second suit consisting of hearts or spades, and a better result will be obtained if he is afforded the opportunity to show it. A one-diamond response allows for this contingency. The worst possible procedure would be to bid one no trump. It is much better to pass than contemplate such a call. Take only half credit if you passed.

5 Pass. Since partner originally passed, there is little to be gained by showing your suit. With six losers in the suits adversely bid, it is inconceivable that you can fulfill an eight-trick contract. In fact, it is difficult to see how you could come close.

6 Double. Even though partner was unwilling to make a free bid, you should still feel bullish about this hand because of your favorable distribution. A bid of two hearts would be improper because it is unnecessary. The double allows for every possibility. Partner may show hearts if he has four, he may bid clubs with length in that suit, he may return to two spades if he prefers, and lastly he might be in a position to pass for penalties if his principal strength is in diamonds. Incidentally, our preferred opening bid would have been one club.

7 Three No Trump. While there is a remote chance that your side can make a slam, I would not be inclined to hold out too much hope. Partner's pass and the vulnerable adverse opening have had a dampening effect. If partner has nothing (not a remote contingency), than even a game contract in diamonds will be out of reach. All things considered, the best bet is to bid three no trump. Take only half credit if you doubled.

8 Seven Spades. You might fool around a while with systems if you feel so inclined, but you must come to only one conclusion and that is that your side can no doubt take all thirteen tricks with spades as trumps. Since partner opened the bidding and jumped, he must be given credit for at least 17 points. You have 20, bringing the combined total to 37, and are only asking for the ace and king of hearts and another king in his hand to justify his bidding. You have no fear of trumps and partner must have a short suit or a good heart suit for discards. Take full credit if your bid was four no trump with the intention of bidding seven spades on the next round.

9 Four No Trump. This is not a Blackwood bid, inasmuch as you are raising partner's no trump, and merely designates that a slam will be available if partner had a maxi-

mum two no trump bid rather than a minimum. (The two-no-trump response designates a hand ranging from 13 to 15 points). Your hand contains 18; if partner happens to have 15, you will have a total of 33, which with a five-card suit should offer you a splendid chance for a slam. If partner has a minimum two-no-trump response, he is at perfect liberty to pass and the contract will not be in jeopardy.

10 The Jack of Clubs. You should resist the temptation to lead hearts even though you have a good sequence and two probable spade entries. The fact that you hold the jack of clubs suggests that your partner's suit can probably be established in one lead and he surely must have an entry. Remember that he bid the suit at the level of three. Remember also that the declarer did not double three clubs, which makes it likely that he has but a single stopper in the suit.

*Your score*_____

1 As South you hold:
  ♠ A J x x x   ♡ x x x   ◇ A K x   ♣ x x
  The bidding has proceeded:

SOUTH	WEST	NORTH	EAST
1 ♠	Pass	1 NT	Pass
?			

  What do you bid now?   Your answer_____

2 As South you hold:
  ♠ x   ♡ A Q J x   ◇ x x   ♣ A K 10 x x x
  The bidding has proceeded:

SOUTH	WEST	NORTH	EAST
1 ♣	Pass	1 ◇	Pass
?			

  What do you bid now?   Your answer_____

3 As South you hold:
  ♠ A   ♡ J 10 x   ◇ A 10 x x x   ♣ J 10 x x
  The bidding has proceeded:

NORTH	EAST	SOUTH	WEST
1 ♡	Pass	2 ◇	Pass
2 ♡	Pass	?	

  What do you bid now?   Your answer_____

4 You are South, vulnerable, and hold:
  ♠ A x x x   ♡ J 10 x   ◇ x   ♣ A x x x x
  The bidding has proceeded:

WEST	NORTH	EAST	SOUTH
1 ◇	1 ♡	Pass	?

  What do you bid?   Your answer_____

5   As South you hold:
    ♠ x   ♡ KQxxx   ◇ Kxx   ♣ AQxx
    The bidding has proceeded:

NORTH	EAST	SOUTH	WEST
2 NT	Pass	3 ♡	Pass
3 ♠	Pass	4 ♣	Pass
4 ◇	Pass	?	

    What do you bid now?   Your answer_____

6   As South you hold:
    ♠ Qxx   ♡ x   ◇ AKxxxx   ♣ Qxx
    The bidding has proceeded:

NORTH	EAST	SOUTH	WEST
1 ♣	Pass	1 ◇	1 ♡
2 ◇	2 ♡	?	

    What do you bid now?   Your answer_____

7   Both sides vulnerable, as South you hold:
    ♠ AJxx   ♡ K10xx   ◇ A   ♣ AQxx
    The bidding has proceeded:

SOUTH	WEST	NORTH	EAST
1 ♣	1 ♡	Pass	1 ♠
?			

    What do you bid now?   Your answer_____

8   As South you hold:
    ♠ 10xxx   ♡ Q10x   ◇ 10xxx   ♣ xx
    The bidding has proceeded:

WEST	NORTH	EAST	SOUTH
1 ◇	Double	Pass	1 ♠
Pass	3 ♡	Pass	?

    What do you bid now?   Your answer_____

9   As South you hold:
    ♠ AQx   ♡ AKQJx   ◇ xxx   ♣ AJ
    The bidding has proceeded:

SOUTH	WEST	NORTH	EAST
1 ♡	Pass	1 ♠	Pass
?			

    What do you bid now?   Your answer_____

43

10 As West you hold:
♠ Q 10 x x ♥ x x ♦ K Q 10 9 x ♣ A x
The bidding has proceeded:

SOUTH	WEST	NORTH	EAST
1 ♦	Pass	3 ♣	Pass
3 NT	Pass	Pass	Pass

What is your opening lead?   Your answer_____

ANSWERS

1 Pass. There is no possible chance for game and the contract should not be increased by rebidding spades. The fact that you are unprotected in two suits should not influence you in this case. Partner's values are probably there. Furthermore, partner may dislike spades intensely. Try for seven tricks by passing.

2 One Heart. The opportunity to show the four-card major at this low range should be seized in preference to rebidding the six-card minor. The impression that a six-card suit must be rebid willy-nilly before showing a four-card suit is a hangover from the Gay Nineties. Take only half credit if your rebid was two clubs.

3 Three Hearts. You should make one effort toward game, and no other satisfactory bid is available. It would be pointless to repeat the diamonds, the hand does not have a no trump "feel," and your hand is worth at least 12 points in support of hearts.

4 Three Hearts. Partner should be given a strong inducement to proceed to game. The lack of robust trumps is no objection to the jump raise, inasmuch as partner's vulnerable overcall must be presumed to advertise a good suit. A big demerit for bidding two clubs, to which partner need not respond, inasmuch as he did not open the bidding. Half credit goes to the chance giving call of two hearts.

5 Seven No Trump. This hand lends itself to simple arithmetic. Your side has just about the entire pack. Partner has indicated by his subsequent bidding that he opened a

44

maximum two no trump, that is to say about 24 points, which added to your 14 equals 38, which should do the trick, particularly with a five-card suit.

6   Five Diamonds. Partner has opened the bidding and made a free raise. He must therefore have a very sound hand. Your queen of clubs has become promoted in value by reason of partner's bid in that suit. You have the right singleton and partner is marked with a high spade as part of his values. You should bid five diamonds and expect to experience no difficulty in making it. Take half credit for a bid of four diamonds.

7   Pass. It is quite apparent that partner has nothing and that "the-snake-in-the-grass game" is your best chance for a profit. Take a demerit if you doubled.

8   Four Hearts. True, you haven't very much, but partner's bidding has indicated that he can probably take close to nine tricks in his own hand. The queen of trumps is a sure winner and the doubleton club should produce a trick for him.

9   Three Clubs. An absolute force to game. Any lesser bid risks playing the hand for a part score. If you make a jump rebid of three hearts, partner will surely pass if he holds nothing but five spades to the king-jack. The same will be true if you jump to three spades. An alternate bid is a jump to four hearts, which is not quite as acceptable but receives eight points since it does obviate any chance of missing a game. If partner happens to have five spades to the king and the ace of diamonds, a slam is very likely, but will not be uncovered unless you make the jump shift recommended above.

10   The King of Diamonds. Even though this suit has been bid, that lead is preferred to the spade. The chances are you will be permitted to hold the trick, in which case both partner's discard and the appearance of the dummy should guide you as to the proper procedure at trick two.

*Your score*_____

1 You hold:
♠ A x x   ♥ 10 x   ♦ Q x x x x   ♣ x x x
Partner opens with two no trump.
What is your response?   Your answer_____

2 As South you hold:
♠ A J x   ♥ A x x   ♦ Q x x x   ♣ 10 x x
The bidding has proceeded:

WEST	NORTH	EAST	SOUTH
1 ♥	1 NT	Pass	?

What do you do now?   Your answer_____

3 As South you hold:
♠ A K x x x   ♥ K x   ♦ x x   ♣ J x x x
The bidding has proceeded:

NORTH	EAST	SOUTH	WEST
1 ♥	Pass	1 ♠	Pass
2 ♥	Pass	?	

What do you bid now?   Your answer_____

4 As South you hold:
♠ J x   ♥ K 10 x   ♦ Q J x x   ♣ 10 x x x
The bidding has proceeded:

NORTH	EAST	SOUTH	WEST
1 ♠	Pass	1 NT	Pass
2 NT	Pass	?	

What do you bid now?   Your answer_____

5 Partner doubles an opening bid of one heart. You hold:
♠ J x x   ♥ Q x x x   ♦ x x x   ♣ x x x
What do you bid?   Your answer_____

6 Partner opens with one heart. You hold:
♠ K J x x   ♥ Q 10 x x   ♦ A K x   ♣ x x
What is your response?   Your answer_____

7 As South you hold:
   ♠ None ♡ A K J x x x ◇ K 10 x x ♣ x x x
   The bidding has proceeded:

SOUTH	WEST	NORTH	EAST
1 ♡	2 ♠	Double	Pass
?			

   What do you bid now?   Your answer_____

8 Partner opens with one club. You hold:
   ♠ A J x x ♡ K 10 x x ◇ x x x ♣ x x
   What do you bid?   Your answer_____

9 Partner opens with one club. You hold:
   ♠ A Q J x ♡ K Q 10 x ◇ x x x ♣ x x
   What do you bid?   Your answer_____

10 As West you hold:
   ♠ K x x ♡ 10 x x x x ◇ K x ♣ Q J 10
   The bidding has proceeded:

SOUTH	WEST	NORTH	EAST
1 NT	Pass	2 NT	Pass
3 NT	Pass	Pass	Pass

   What is your opening lead?   Your answer_____

ANSWERS

1 Three No Trump. Since partner's maximum high-card
   value is 24 points, there is no reasonable hope for a slam
   and nothing is to be gained by showing the diamond suit
   with only 6 points. A mere raise to three no trump is
   indicated.

2 Partner's overcall of one no trump should be treated as
   though it were an opening bid of one no trump. You
   should therefore raise to three, inasmuch as you have 11
   points. A raise to two would not be adequate and partner
   might refuse to carry on.

3 Three Hearts. Game-going prospects are bright because
   you have almost the equal of an opening bid, facing partner's opening bid. Your minor-suit holding precludes a

no-trump try, and it would be pointless to rebid spades, which partner might not like. Your trump support is adequate for a rebid suit.

4 Three No Trump. On casual analysis it should seem that you had already said a mouthful when you responded with one no trump, but actually your hand is better than it would seem to be on the surface. It contains a point count of 7 without counting the value of the tens, and the jack of spades assumes a greater value by reason of partner's bid in that suit. We recommend going to three no trump. As far as partner knows, you may have only 6 points.

5 It behooves you to find the cheapest way out of an awkward situation and that way is by a call of one spade. Don't bid one no trump, which would be far more dangerous. And hide your face in the corner if you passed from fright.

6 Three Hearts. This hand is just about the equal of an opening bid and has ample trump support; consequently you are in a position to insist upon a game. The most expedient manner in which to do this is by a jump to three hearts. There is nothing to be gained by making a temporizing bid of one spade on this hand, since a future bidding problem might develop if you do so. Take only half credit for one spade.

7 While partner's double is for penalties, we nevertheless do not recommend that you stand for the double. Your hand will be a disappointment defensively, yet has some offensive merit, and a rebid of three hearts is our choice.

8 One Heart, rather than one spade. This permits partner to show a four-card spade suit at the level of one if he happens to have it. Whereas if you respond with one spade, partner may have a four-card heart suit and fear to show it at the level of two. Take only half credit for one spade.

9 One Spade. This hand differs from the preceding one in that it possesses sufficient strength to justify your bidding twice opposite a partner who was able to open the bid-

ding. Since you will be able to show both suits yourself, you should do so in the normal order.

10 A Small Heart. The normal opening of your long suit should be selected, inasmuch as you have at least two entries. This is not the type of hand on which to make a short-suit lead. The lead of the queen of clubs is our second choice and is awarded half credit.

*Your score*_____

1 Partner opens with one spade. You hold:
   ♠ x x ♡ A x x ◇ A 10 x x ♣ A x x x
   What do you bid?   Your answer_____

2 As South you hold:
   ♠ A x ♡ K x ◇ A K J x x x ♣ Q J x
   The bidding has proceeded:
   SOUTH WEST NORTH EAST
   1 ◇   Pass 2 NT   Pass
   ?
   What do you bid now?   Your answer_____

3 As South you hold:
   ♠ A K x x ♡ 10 x x ◇ A x x ♣ Q x x
   The bidding has proceeded:
   NORTH EAST SOUTH WEST
   Pass   Pass 1 ♠   Pass
   2 ♡   Pass ?
   What do you bid now?   Your answer_____

4 Partner opens with one no trump. You hold:
   ♠ x ♡ A x x x ◇ K Q 10 x x x ♣ 10 x
   What is your response?   Your answer_____

5 As South you hold:
   ♠ K x ♡ K J x x ◇ A J x x ♣ K x x
   The bidding has proceeded:
   NORTH EAST SOUTH WEST
   1 ♠   Pass 2 NT   Pass
   4 NT   Pass ?
   What do you bid now?   Your answer_____

6 As South you hold:
   ♠ xxxxxx ♡ Ax ◇ 10x ♣ AJx
   The bidding has proceeded:

NORTH	EAST	SOUTH	WEST
1 ♣	Pass	1 ♠	Pass
2 ♠	Pass	?	

   What do you bid now?   Your answer_____

7 As South you hold:
   ♠ AKQx ♡ xx ◇ KJ ♣ J10xxx
   The bidding has proceeded:

EAST	SOUTH	WEST	NORTH
4 ♡	Pass	Pass	4 ♠
Pass	?		

   What do you bid now?   Your answer_____

8 You are South and hold:
   ♠ xx ♡ xx ◇ Qxxxx ♣ AKQ10
   The bidding has proceeded:

NORTH	EAST	SOUTH	WEST
1 ♠	Pass	2 ◇	Pass
4 ◇	Pass	?	

   What do you bid now?   Your answer_____

9 You are South and hold:
   ♠ J ♡ KJx ◇ Jxx ♣ Qxxxxx
   The bidding has proceeded:

EAST	SOUTH	WEST	NORTH
1 ♡	Pass	Pass	Double
Pass	2 ♣	Pass	3 ♣
Pass	?		

   What do you bid now?   Your answer_____

10   As West you hold:
    ♠ J 10 6 5 2   ♡ Q 7 3   ◇ 5 2   ♣ A 6 4
    The bidding has proceeded:

EAST	SOUTH	WEST	NORTH
1 ♡	1 NT	Pass	2 NT
Pass	3 NT	Pass	Pass
Pass			

    What is your opening lead?   Your answer_____

ANSWERS

1   Two Diamonds or Two Clubs. This hand is just an eye-lash short of the high-card value for a two-no-trump response. Such a bid calls for 13 to 15 points in high cards. As the hand is constructed, we would not be inclined to make an immediate guarantee of game, but should like to suggest it by first bidding two of a suit and then following with two no trump if partner rebids two spades. Take only half credit if your bid was two no trump.

2   Our vote is for six no trump. You have a good trick and a half more than your opening bid and the combined partners' assets are in the neighborhood of 33 points. They may be a little less if partner has a minimum two-no-trump response, but with a six-card suit, considerable enemy ammunition may be rendered useless.

3   Pass. Inasmuch as partner has previously passed, you should be convinced that you are not going places. This is definitely a part-score hand and there is nothing wrong with hearts as trump. A bid of two no trump would be more than wishful thinking and receives a demerit.

4   Three Diamonds. There is no doubt that you must insist upon a game contract, and it would appear at first glance that you should use the two-club convention in search of a possible heart contract. Better strategy is to make the jump response of three diamonds, which will serve exactly the same purpose. It has the added advantage of allowing for the possibility of playing the hand in a diamond game, or slam for that matter. If partner opened

the bidding with a hand that contained a four-card heart suit, he may show it at no cost over your three-diamond bid. If he shows a four-card spade suit, you will return to three no trump. If he rebids three no trump, you will pass. Take only half credit if your response was three no trump.

5 Six No Trump. This is not to be interpreted as a Blackwood call, even though a suit has been mentioned. A four-no-trump bid is not to be construed as a quest for aces, when partner has previously made a voluntary no-trump bid. It is merely a plain common-sense raise of the no trump. Partner has invited you to bid a slam if you have a maximum two-no-trump response. Such a response is made on hands ranging from 13 to 15 points. You have 15, which is as much as partner could expect, and you should bid six no trump. Take no credit if you bid five diamonds.

6 Four Spades. The combined partnership assets amount to two opening bids. By his raise partner has shown a minimum of 14 points in support of spades. Your hand is worth 14 points (remember—add 1 point for the fifth trump and 2 points for each additional trump after a raise from partner). The texture of your trump suit should not frighten you; partner has at least three and perhaps four spades so that you have a minimum of nine between you. Take half credit if you bid only three spades.

7 Five Spades. Partner must have exceptional values to be able to compete at this level with a suit that is at best jack-high. Your hand should produce a minimum of four tricks for him, so that a contract of five should be reasonably safe even if partner happens to be romancing. The chance for a slam should not be overlooked.

8 You have very close to the equal of an opening bid. Partner has opened the bidding and jumped, which spells slam. The recommended call is five clubs. If partner merely returns to five diamonds, you may retire, but he

should be given some inducement to consider a slam. Take only half credit if you bid five diamonds.

9   Three No Trump. Up to this point you have shown no values other than length in clubs, and partner has invited you to proceed. While an eleven-trick contract is probably not obtainable against the opening bid, a nine-trick contract at no trump should readily be fulfilled since you have a double stopper in hearts. Possession of a singleton spade should not deter you from no trump, since partner by his take-out double has designated distributed values which indubitably include some high cards in spades. Four clubs is worth five points.

10 A Small Heart. Even though no trump has been bid immediately over your partner's hearts, you should select that suit, since you have an important supporting card. The two is the correct lead, because the declarer might have the king-jack-small or ace-jack-small, and the lead of the queen would permit him to take two tricks.

*Your score*_____

QUIZ 13

1 As South you hold:
♠ Q x x ♡ x x ◇ A Q x ♣ A J x x x
The bidding has proceeded:

NORTH	EAST	SOUTH	WEST
1 ♠	Pass	2 ♣	Pass
2 ♡	Pass	?	

What do you bid now?   Your answer_____

2 As dealer you hold:
♠ A J x ♡ K Q x ◇ A Q x x ♣ A J x
What do you bid?   Your answer_____

3 As dealer, vulnerable, you hold:
♠ None ♡ Q J 10 x x x x x ◇ x ♣ Q J 10 x
What do you bid?   Your answer_____

4 As South, vulnerable, you hold:
♠ A K x ♡ K Q x ◇ A x x x ♣ J x x
The bidding has proceeded:

NORTH	EAST	SOUTH	WEST
1 ♣	1 ♠	?	

What do you bid?   Your answer_____

5 You are South and hold:
♠ K 10 x x x ♡ x x ◇ A 10 x x ♣ x x
The bidding has proceeded:

WEST	NORTH	EAST	SOUTH
1 ♡	2 ♣	Pass	?

What do you bid?   Your answer_____

55

6 You are South and hold:
   ♠ xxxx ♡ Q 10 xxx ◇ 10 x ♣ Ax
   The bidding has proceeded:

WEST	NORTH	EAST	SOUTH
1 ◇	Double	2 ◇	?

   What do you bid?   Your answer_____

7 As South you hold:
   ♠ Kx ♡ KQxxx ◇ AJx ♣ xxx
   The bidding has proceeded:

NORTH	EAST	SOUTH	WEST
1 ♠	Pass	2 ♡	Pass
4 ♣	Pass	4 ◇	Pass
6 ♡	Pass	?	

   What do you bid now?   Your answer_____

8 As South you hold:
   ♠ KJ ♡ Jxxx ◇ Qx ♣ Jxxxx
   The bidding has proceeded:

NORTH	EAST	SOUTH	WEST
1 ♠	Pass	1 NT	Pass
2 ◇	Pass	2 ♠	Pass
3 ♠	Pass	?	

   What do you bid now?   Your answer_____

9 Opponents vulnerable, you are not. You are South and
   hold:
   ♠ 10 xxx ♡ xxxx ◇ Axx ♣ Ax
   The bidding has proceeded:

NORTH	EAST	SOUTH	WEST
1 ♣	1 ♡	Pass	Pass
Double	2 ♡	?	

   What do you bid now?   Your answer_____

10 As West you hold:
    ♠ A Q J x x   ♡ x x x   ◇ K J x   ♣ x x
    The bidding has proceeded:

SOUTH	WEST	NORTH	EAST
1 ♣	1 ♠	1 NT	Pass
3 ♡	Pass	3 NT	Pass
6 ♣	Pass	Pass	Pass

What is your opening lead?   Your answer_____

ANSWERS

1   Three No Trump. Naturally a jump bid is obligatory at this point, but a jump in spades is not recommended, inasmuch as you have only three trumps. Such a bid should rarely be made without four. There is the additional consideration that you should strain to be declarer to protect your diamond tenace against immediate attack. If partner has a minimum hand without freakish distribution, there will be no slam. If he has excess values, he should bid again, at which point you may decide whether to support spades or show the diamond control. Take half credit if you rebid three spades.

2   One Diamond. Despite the appropriate distribution, an opening bid of one no trump would be improper. The hand is too strong for such a call. Eighteen points is the absolute limit and this hand contains 21, which renders it just an eyelash short of a two no trump opening. All such hands should be opened with one of a suit with the intention of jumping in no trump if partner responds.

3   Four Hearts. You have the ability to take eight tricks in your own hand and should open the bidding with four hearts. Even if partner does not produce a trick for you, the limit of loss is 500. And in that case, the opponents will surely have a game and very likely a slam. There is the further consideration that partner needs very little for you to make four hearts, if it happens to be in the right spots. A bid of only three hearts is a step in the right

direction and gets half credit. A pass is evidence of faint-heartedness, for which we designate one demerit.

4 Three No Trump. There are several choices open to South, but this is our choice because in one fell swoop it gives a complete picture of the hand both as to point count and distribution. Partner will then become the one who knows whether or not there is a slam in the air. If he has a minimum, he passes with no earthly cares; if he has any excess values or abnormal distribution, he knows he may expect from 16 to 18 points from you and may act accordingly. A cue bid of two spades would be quite acceptable. Take half credit for a bid of two diamonds. No credit is awarded to a double.

5 There is no need for you to keep the bidding open. Partner has not invited you to co-operate. If he wished you to bid, he would make a take-out double. A bid of two spades would not be safe, and if partner should be obliged to return to three clubs, you would not find it to your taste. We suggest that you pass.

6 Two Hearts. When partner has made a take-out double, considerable latitude is permitted in making free bids. This, on the surface, is not an impressive hand, but any hand containing a five-card suit with more than 7 points should be considered a good hand when held by the partner of the doubler. Therefore, we recommend a bid of two hearts.

7 Seven Hearts (unless there is some doubt in your mind as to partner's trustworthiness). His bidding has announced a hand of huge proportion. Your previous bids would have been justified without the king of spades, and partner is willing to predict that you can win twelve tricks merely on the basis of your hearts and diamonds. Surely he must have been allowing for the loss of a trick to the king of spades and on that basis your grand-slam call is justified.

8 Four Spades. Partner knows you have a weak hand, inasmuch as you have twice failed to make a constructive bid. Yet he still thinks there may be a chance for game. He no doubt has two five-card suits and is therefore not very

long in hearts and clubs. Your holding in spades and diamonds will take care of a number of partner's losers. They are almost the equivalent of aces.

9 Double. Your hand should develop three tricks and partner should take four in view of his bidding. This means a two-trick penalty, or 500 points. Four small trumps should be regarded as a defensive trick.

10 A Small Diamond. Unless partner has the queen of diamonds, your cause is lost. You must establish a diamond trick before dummy's king of spades is established.

*Your score*_____

QUIZ 14

1 As dealer you hold:
   ♠ A J x x   ♡ Q x x   ◇ J x x x x   ♣ A
   What is your opening bid?   Your answer_____

2 Partner opens with one club and you hold:
   ♠ A Q 10   ♡ K Q x   ◇ A 10 x x   ♣ J x x
   What is your response?   Your answer_____

3 As South you hold:
   ♠ K Q 10 x   ♡ x   ◇ A J x x   ♣ K x x
   The bidding has proceeded:
   WEST   NORTH   EAST   SOUTH
   1 ♠   Pass   Pass   ?
   What is your bid?   Your answer_____

4 As South you hold:
   ♠ A 10 x x   ♡ K J x x x   ◇ Q   ♣ A Q x
   The bidding has proceeded:
   NORTH   EAST   SOUTH   WEST
   1 ◇   Pass   1 ♡   Pass
   2 ♣   Pass   2 ♠   Pass
   3 NT   Pass   ?
   What do you bid now?   Your answer_____

5 As South you hold:
   ♠ A Q 10 x x   ♡ K J x   ◇ x x x   ♣ x x
   The bidding has proceeded:
   NORTH   EAST   SOUTH   WEST
   1 ♡   2 ◇   ?
   What do you bid?   Your answer_____

6 As South you hold:
   ♠ K x x   ♡ A Q x   ◇ 10 x   ♣ A K Q x x
   The bidding has proceeded:

WEST	NORTH	EAST	SOUTH
1 ♠	Pass	Pass	Double
Pass	2 ◇	Pass	?

   What do you bid now?   Your answer_____

7 As South you hold:
   ♠ A Q x x x   ♡ A J x x   ◇ Q x   ♣ J x
   The bidding has proceeded:

NORTH	EAST	SOUTH	WEST
1 ◇	Pass	1 ♠	Pass
2 ♣	Pass	?	

   What do you bid now?   Your answer_____

8 As South you hold:
   ♠ A K x x   ♡ Q x   ◇ A K 10   ♣ K J x x
   The bidding has proceeded:

SOUTH	WEST	NORTH	EAST
1 ♣	Pass	1 ♡	Pass
2 NT	Pass	3 ♡	Pass
3 NT	Pass	4 NT	Pass
?			

   What do you bid now?   Your answer_____

9 As South you hold:
   ♠ A K x x   ♡ A Q x x   ◇ K J x x   ♣ 5
   The bidding has proceeded:

SOUTH	WEST	NORTH	EAST
1 ♠	Pass	2 NT	Pass
3 ♡	Pass	3 NT	Pass
?			

   What do you bid now?   Your answer_____

10 As West you hold:
♠ None ♡ x x x ◇ Q J 10 x x x ♣ x x x x
The bidding has proceeded:

SOUTH	WEST	NORTH	EAST
1 ♠	Pass	3 ♣	3 ♡
3 ♠	Pass	4 ♠	Pass
6 ♠	Pass	Pass	Double
Pass	Pass	Pass	

What is your opening lead?   Your answer_____

ANSWERS

1   In order to be comfortably prepared for any response partner may make, the spade suit should be selected for the opening bid. If partner makes the expected response of two clubs, a convenient rebid of two diamonds is available. If partner responds with two hearts, you are in position to offer a single raise. To state the principle underlying these hands in the form of a rule, weak five-card suits should be treated as though they were four-card suits. If your diamonds were only four cards long, the proper opening bid would be the suit below the singleton, that is to say, one spade. Take half credit for a one-diamond opening.

2   It would be poor strategy to approach with a bid of one diamond, which would lead only to a future problem. There is a bid especially devised for this type of hand, that is, one that is evenly balanced and contains 16 points; it is three no trump. Thus in one round of bidding partner will be able to calculate the exact high-card holding of the partnership. Do not make the mistake of responding with only two no trump, which describes a hand ranging in high-card content between 13 and 15. A bid of one diamond is not altogether wrong and is awarded three points.

3   Pass. Although as a rule it is not good policy to permit the opposition to buy a hand this cheaply, when they are playing it in your best suit you should be slow to disturb

them. If you should double, it is very likely that partner will have to bid hearts, which might prove embarrassing.

4 Four Clubs. This bid is preparatory to bidding six no trump, the safety of which we have no doubt. But there may be great things in store for us and we had better tell all. Take only half credit if you rebid six no trump, a bid which leaves partner no chance but to pass.

5 Two Hearts. This hand contains distinct offensive values but not quite enough to insist upon a game. You should therefore make a bid which shows a desire to go forward without committing your partnership to a game contract. The suggested call is a free raise to two hearts which designates a moderate holding. A bid of two spades, while it appears inviting, should be avoided. Such action will almost certainly force your partnership into a game contract even with a minimum holding. For if partner rebids three hearts, which he may be obliged to do, surely you intend to go to four, without knowledge that he has any additional values.

6 It would be poor tactics to show the club suit since the one hope for game lies in no trump. The suggested call is two no trump; if partner has any sign of assistance, he will take you to three. A leap to three no trump would be totally unjustified, for North has been forced to bid and may not have anything in the way of high-card strength.

7 Three No Trump. There can be no possible doubt in your mind that there is game in the hand, and it should be quite evident that the game is in no trump. It is suggested, therefore, that you make your jump bid in the denomination that best suits your hand as a whole, and that is no trump. We favor a bid of three no trump and see nothing to be gained by approaching further with a bid of two hearts. Since partner has two minor suits, he can hardly have support for your four-card heart suit, and the no-trump contract rates to play better from your side than from his. A heart bid will put him in position where he may have to bid the no trump himself.

8 Partner's four-no-trump bid should not be construed as a

Blackwood call but a simple raise of your previously mentioned no-trump bid and an invitation to go to slam. This invitation you should accept with alacrity. First, because you have a full point more than you needed to justify your jump rebid to two no trump; second, your queen of hearts has become promoted to the value of a king, so that gives you another point. Then too, partner has assured you that you will be able to run a long heart suit. Our vote is for six no trump.

9 Four Diamonds. Hope for a slam should not be abandoned. It is doubtful that the partnership possesses enough honor strength for a no-trump slam, for you have 17 points and partner's maximum is 15. But a slam in diamonds is by no means remote, for it is not at all unlikely that partner holds four of that suit, in which case your side can avail itself of the advantages of the favorable distribution. The suggested bid is, therefore, four diamonds. This will advise partner that you have a three-suiter with definite excess values, and will place him in good position to decide the subsequent action.

10 A Club. You must not lead your partner's suit or the unbid suit because the double of the slam contract calls for the first suit the dummy has bid. Your partner can ruff the opening lead and defeat the contract with his heart trick.

*Your score*_____

1 You are third hand after two passes, and hold:
   ♠ A K 10 x ♡ J x x ◇ x x x ♣ A J x
   What do you bid?   Your answer_____

2 As South you hold:
   ♠ x x x ♡ A x x ◇ K x x x ♣ J x x
   The bidding has proceeded:
   NORTH   EAST   SOUTH   WEST
   1 ♠   Double   ?
   What do you bid?   Your answer_____

3 Both sides vulnerable, you are South and hold:
   ♠ J x ♡ A x x ◇ Q 10 x x ♣ K 10 x x
   The bidding has proceeded:
   NORTH   EAST   SOUTH   WEST
   1 ♠   2 ◇   ?
   What do you bid?   Your answer_____

4 As South you hold:
   ♠ Q 10 x x ♡ K J x x x ◇ x x ♣ x x
   The bidding has proceeded:
   NORTH   EAST   SOUTH   WEST
   1 ◇   Double   ?
   What do you bid?   Your answer_____

5 As South you hold:
   ♠ x x ♡ 10 x x ◇ K J x x ♣ K J x x
   The bidding has proceeded:
   SOUTH   WEST   NORTH   EAST
   Pass   Pass   1 ♡   1 ♠
   ?
   What do you bid?   Your answer_____

6 As South you hold:
   ♠ AJxx ♡ Jx ◇ Jxxx ♣ Qxx
   The bidding has proceeded:
   NORTH EAST SOUTH WEST
   2 ♣   2 ♠   ?
   What do you bid?   Your answer_____

7 As South you hold:
   ♠ x ♡ QJxx ◇ 10xxx ♣ AQxx
   The bidding has proceeded:
   SOUTH WEST NORTH EAST
   Pass   Pass 1 ♡   Pass
   ?
   What do you bid now?   Your answer_____

8 As South you hold:
   ♠ KJxx ♡ Qxxxx ◇ A10x ♣ A
   The bidding has proceeded:
   EAST SOUTH WEST NORTH
   1 ♡   Pass   Pass 1 ♠
   Pass ?
   What do you bid now?   Your answer_____

9 You are vulnerable, opponents not, and as South you
   hold:
   ♠ AJ ♡ KJx ◇ KQx ♣ AQxxx
   The bidding has proceeded:
   WEST NORTH EAST SOUTH
   1 ♠   2 ♡   3 ♠   ?
   What do you bid?   Your answer_____

10 As West you hold:
   ♠ J10xx ♡ x ◇ AQxxx ♣ Qxx
   The bidding has proceeded:
   NORTH EAST SOUTH WEST
   1 ♣   Pass 1 ♡   Pass
   2 NT   Pass 3 ♠   Pass
   4 ♠   Pass Pass   Pass
   What is your opening lead?   Your answer_____

ANSWERS

1 One Spade, trying for a part score and intending to pass any response by partner other than a jump in a new suit, which is considered forcing for one round. It is unnecessary to open with a club in third position, since you need not prepare for a rebid.

2 One No Trump. Your hand contains some values and your partner may be interested to know you have something, should he be anxious to contest the hand for a part score. This is the only convenient time you will have to advise him of your slight possessions. If you pass, the bidding is bound to get up too high before you can speak safely. You should, therefore, bid one no trump immediately. This just about describes the strength of your hand. Take only half credit for a pass.

3 Double. Resist the impulse to bid two no trump in favor of wielding the ax. Your own hand will produce at least four tricks against the diamond contract, and partner may be counted on to produce three, which is a sure set of 500 points, with the possibility of a greater harvest if partner has a better hand. Furthermore, if partner has a minimum hand, you will probably not be able to make game.

4 One Heart. This hand contains barely enough in values to justify making your presence known in a mild sort of manner. It is highly improbable that there will be any convenient opportunity to bid later in the day, so that you must speak now or forever hold your peace. To pass with the idea that the opposition may bid aggressively into one of your suits is rather too sanguine. The suggested call is, therefore, one heart.

5 Two Hearts. We naturally prefer to have better trump support, but this is the least of evils. In view of our previous pass, it is desirable to take some action and no other is available. To pass again might result in partner giving

up the fight on a hand in which a part score could be scored easily. A bid of two diamonds or two clubs is a distinct overbid and receives a demerit.

6   Three Clubs. Opposite a partner who has announced that he has within a trick of game in his own hand, you have good reason to suspect a slam. The proper procedure is to give an immediate raise in clubs to allay any doubts partner may have as to the solidity of the trump suit. It is your full intention to show the ace of spades on the next round. An immediate raise in clubs is superior to a bid in no trump, and a double of two spades may not prove sufficiently profitable, but is awarded half credit because it is a move in a positive direction.

7   Since you have previously passed, you can afford to make a more or less drastic bid, and the suggested call is three hearts. Under the circumstances, this bid is not forcing. If partner has a light opening, he may refuse to go on. If he has a good hand, he should have a fair chance for game. A bid of two clubs would be improper because partner, recalling your previous pass, might not bid again. Take half credit for a raise to two hearts and no credit for bidding four hearts, a call which in a sense has punished partner if his opening bid was made with a part score in mind.

8   While it is known from partner's failure to double that he has not a strong hand, nevertheless his hand must have some merit since he could have passed one heart, yet he preferred not to let "sleeping dogs lie." Since your hand is worth 17 points in support, you should go all the way to four spades. If you bid only three, partner may not be able to carry on with a below-average hand.

9   It must have become evident to you by this time that West is lying through his teeth. There aren't enough cards in the deck to justify all this activity around the table. Your partner, vulnerable, must be telling the truth. All he needs is a decent five-card heart suit and one other high card to make a slam. Since the enemy has deprived you of the normal means of conversation, you must pull your-

self together and bid six hearts. You could stop off on the way to cue bid four spades if you like.

10 The Ace of Diamonds. Having four trumps, you should try to establish a force on the declarer by leading your longest suit. The two-no-trump bid has indicated that the king of diamonds is probably behind you in the dummy. Therefore, your lead of the ace will probably not cost a trick.

*Your score*_____

1 As dealer you hold:
   ♠ A J 10 x ♡ K Q x x ◇ A x x x ♣ x
   What is your opening bid?   Your answer_____

2 As dealer you hold:
   ♠ J 10 x x x ♡ A K ◇ K 10 x ♣ x x x
   What is your opening bid?   Your answer_____

3 Both sides are vulnerable. You are South and hold:
   ♠ x x x x ♡ x ◇ A K x x x ♣ K Q x
   The bidding has proceeded:
   | WEST | NORTH | EAST | SOUTH |
   | 1 ♠ | 2 ♡ | Double | ? |
   What do you bid?   Your answer_____

4 As South you hold:
   ♠ J x x ♡ x x x x ◇ A K x ♣ Q J x
   The bidding has proceeded:
   | WEST | NORTH | EAST | SOUTH |
   | 1 ♠ | Double | 3 ♠ | ? |
   What do you bid?   Your answer_____

5 Opponents have 60 part score. You are South and hold:
   ♠ K J x x x ♡ x ◇ K Q J x ♣ x x x
   The bidding has proceeded:
   | WEST | NORTH | EAST | SOUTH |
   | 3 ♡ | Double | Pass | ? |
   What do you bid?   Your answer_____

6 As South you hold:
   ♠ A x ♡ K x x x ◇ J 10 x ♣ A J x x
   The bidding has proceeded:
   | NORTH | EAST | SOUTH | WEST |
   | 1 NT | 2 ◇ | ? | |
   What do you bid now?   Your answer_____

7   Partner opens fourth hand with one diamond. You hold:
    ♠ K x ♡ Q J x ◇ K 10 x x x x ♣ K x
    What do you bid?   Your answer_____

8   As South you hold:
    ♠ A Q 10 x ♡ x x ◇ x x x ♣ A J x x
    The bidding has proceeded:

NORTH	EAST	SOUTH	WEST
1 ♣	Pass	1 ♠	Pass
2 ♡	Pass	3 ♣	Pass
3 ♠	Pass	?	

    What do you bid now?   Your answer_____

9   As South you hold:
    ♠ K x x x ♡ A K x x x ◇ None ♣ K J x x
    The bidding has proceeded:

NORTH	EAST	SOUTH	WEST
1 ♠	2 ◇	?	

    What do you bid?   Your answer_____

10 As West you hold:
    ♠ Q x x ♡ K x x ◇ J x x x x x ♣ x
    The bidding has proceeded:

SOUTH	WEST	NORTH	EAST
1 ♣	Pass	1 ◇	1 ♠
3 ♡	Pass	4 ♡	Pass
Pass	Pass		

    What is your opening lead?   Your answer_____

ANSWERS

1   One Spade. The suit below the singleton; spades are con-
    sidered to rank below clubs for the purpose of this rule.
    Take only half credit if your bid was one heart or one
    diamond.

2   Pass. Your hand has the value of only 12 points for a
    suit bid of one, and should not be opened. Furthermore,
    the hand does not contain a rebiddable suit.

3   Unless your partner is one who has delusions of grandeur,

smile inwardly. Somebody has done something wrong, and with your high-card holding, partner should surely score eight tricks even though the trumps are banked against him. A rescue to three diamonds would border on the absurd, especially when game is the reward for partner's fulfilled contract. A pass is in order.

4 East's bid has placed you in an awkward position. Holding more than two and a half honor tricks, you may readily visualize a game when partner doubles. However, it is rather touchy to contract for game in hearts with such an emaciated trump suit. While I would not condemn a bid of four hearts, my own preference with an understanding partner is to double. He will realize that I am not doubling on spade strength and if he has a long suit he should bid it. Take five points if your bid was four hearts.

5 Partner's double of the opening pre-emptive bid should be construed as a take-out double, and I believe you should insist upon a game contract, by bidding the game in spades yourself. If you should bid only three spades, partner will in all probability have to pass, not knowing whether or not you have any values. This would be especially true if he happened to have made a doubtful double in view of the adverse score. You ought to be able to make ten tricks even opposite a light take-out double.

6 Someone has committed an indiscretion and you should assume that it is East. Capitalize on it by making a mercenary double. If partner is honest, this will be one to remember.

7 Three No Trump. This is a rare occurrence, but the hand calls for it. Any lesser bid may be passed by partner, who will bear in mind that you were unable to open the bidding. A jump to three diamonds would be poor strategy, first because partner would probably pass, and second, if the hand is to be played at no trump, you should be declarer to protect your spade and club kings against the opening lead. Take half credit if you bid two no trump.

8   A jump bid by you is clearly indicated. Up to this point you have not yet made an aggressive move. Your first response of one spade promised no great values and then when partner made the reverse bid of two hearts, advertising great strength, you merely returned to his first suit under pressure. Partner presumably has five clubs, four hearts, and three spades, leaving him with but a single diamond. To show that your suits contain important honors, you should jump at this point. Anything less than a bid of five clubs would suggest the presence of a timid soul. Full credit is awarded to a bid of six clubs.

9   You have several choices. You might make an immediate cue bid forcing to game and announcing slam aspirations. You might make a jump-shift response of three hearts, also a slam signal, or you might temporize with a mere one-round force of two hearts. My own preference is for the latter. The reason for the choice is that there are a number of features about this hand that it will be desirable to describe, and it is well to provide sufficient bidding space for all these anticipated maneuvers. This leaves a cue bid in reserve for a later round. A three-spade bid would not be accepted as correct, for if partner makes the natural rebid of four spades, it will necessitate your initiating your slam conversation at the level of five.

10 The Club. Here the singleton should be preferred to the lead of your partner's suit. You have the ideal condition for such a lead: a trump stopper and one superfluous trump and the ability to give your partner the lead to obtain the ruff. Take only half credit if you led a spade.

*Your score*_____

1 As South you hold:
  ♠ A Q ♡ Q 10 x ◇ K J x x ♣ A J 10 x
  The bidding has proceeded:
  EAST SOUTH WEST NORTH
  1 ♣   ?
  What do you bid?   Your answer_____

2 As South you hold:
  ♠ Q x x x ♡ x x ◇ x x x ♣ A Q 10 x
  The bidding has proceeded:
  NORTH EAST SOUTH WEST
  1 ♠   Pass 2 ♠   Pass
  2 NT   Pass ?
  What do you bid now?   Your answer_____

3 Partner opens with one diamond and you hold:
  ♠ A J x ♡ K J x ◇ Q 10 x x ♣ K x x
  What is your response?   Your answer_____

4 As South you hold:
  ♠ A K x ♡ x x ◇ x x x ♣ Q J x x x
  The bidding has proceeded:
  NORTH EAST SOUTH WEST
  1 ♠   Pass 2 ♣   Pass
  2 ♡   Pass ?
  What do you bid now?   Your answer_____

5 As South you hold:
  ♠ 10 x x ♡ x x x ◇ A J x x x ♣ K x
  The bidding has proceeded:
  NORTH EAST SOUTH WEST
  1 ♠   2 ♡   ?
  What do you bid?   Your answer_____

6 Both sides are vulnerable. You are South and hold:
   ♠ 10xxx ♡ AJ10x ◇ Q ♣ AQxx
   The bidding has proceeded:

EAST	SOUTH	WEST	NORTH
1 ♣	Pass	1 ♡	2 ◇
2 ♠	?		

   What do you bid now?   Your answer_____

7 As South you hold:
   ♠ K10xx ♡ 109 ◇ AQx ♣ AQJx
   The bidding has proceeded:

SOUTH	WEST	NORTH	EAST
1 ♣	Pass	3 NT	Pass
?			

   What do you bid now?   Your answer_____

8 As South you hold:
   ♠ x ♡ Axxx ◇ QJxx ♣ K10xx
   The bidding has proceeded:

NORTH	EAST	SOUTH	WEST
1 ♣	Pass	1 ◇	1 ♡
3 ♣	Pass	?	

   What do you bid now?   Your answer_____

9 As South you hold:
   ♠ Ax ♡ AQJx ◇ Jxx ♣ AJxx
   The bidding has proceeded:

SOUTH	WEST	NORTH	EAST
1 ♣	Pass	1 ◇	Pass
1 ♡	Pass	2 ♣	Pass
?			

   What do you bid now?   Your answer_____

10 As West you hold:
   ♠ AKx ♡ A10x ◇ J10 ♣ QJxxx
   The bidding has proceeded:

SOUTH	WEST	NORTH	EAST
1 ♡	Double	3 ♡	3 ♠
4 ♡	Double	Pass	Pass

   What is your opening lead?   Your answer_____

ANSWERS

1 With hands of this type and strength it is our policy to give a complete description of the holding in one bid, and that is one no trump. This announces a hand on which South could have opened with one no trump had East passed, and also promises ample protection in the adverse suit. South has a point count of 17 and a balanced hand, which qualifies it as a normal one-no-trump hand.

2 You should contract for game. Your original response announced a hand of only moderate strength, and yet partner was unwilling to quit. His rebid states that he wishes you to go on to game if you had a good raise rather than a courtesy raise. Actually your hand contains the maximum values on which a single raise is proper. Your proper bid is, therefore, four spades. A mere return to three spades would denote a preference for spades over no trump but would announce that your raise had been made on a weak hand.

3 Only one response can be considered and that is the very natural bid of two no trump, forcing to game. You have a balanced hand, which is the equal in strength of an opening bid (14 points), and it is not necessary to make any approach bid. A response of three diamonds would have nothing to gain and would not paint a precise picture as to the type of holding you have.

4 The proper call is two spades. Some players will bolt at this suggestion on the ground that, as they put it, this would be a mere preference instead of a raise. It doesn't much matter by what name you call it; partner will realize that you have a fairly good hand from the fact that you first took the trouble to bid two clubs, a call which showed better than an average hand in strength.

5 Here again no completely satisfactory call is available. One thing is certain; South may not bid three diamonds. The choice lies between passing and offering a single

raise. Our own tastes run slightly toward the latter, though it is admittedly a very close case. Perhaps it is bad pedagogy to show again an example of raising with less than the standard trump support, but I feel it my duty to present these cases to my constituents as they come up. I'll try to have better trumps in the future.

6   Double. It is very evident that West must have made a very light one-over-one or this is a pinochle deck. The enemy is now in severe difficulties. You have the first suit all bottled up. You have probably as many trumps as the bidder. You have dummy's suit well taken care of and then there is partner to be taken account of. He made a vulnerable overcall against two bidding players with a passing partner. The recommended call is a double. If your partner has a very unbalanced hand and refuses to stand for the double, you need not be concerned because the queen of diamonds assures you that your trump suit will be in good order.

7   Four No Trump (not Blackwood). Your hand possesses extra values over and above those required for the opening bid and they are well distributed. Partner's response describes a hand on which he could have opened with one no trump had he dealt; in other words, a minimum of 16 points, which added to your 16 makes a total of 32, placing you on the threshold of a slam. You should raise your partner above the game in no trump. If he has a minimum, he will pass; if he has any slight excess, he should try for six.

8   Three Hearts. This has become a much more impressive hand than when you first gazed upon it. In view of the promoted value of your club holding and the singleton spade in support of partner's suit, you have a hand that in playing strength is the equal of an opening bid. Since partner has opened and jumped, it behooves you to become mildly slam-conscious. The way to designate such an attitude is to make a cue bid of three hearts and await partner's next move. A mere raise to four clubs would be inadequate.

9   Two No Trump. Up to this point nothing much has taken place on either side of the table. So far as you can tell, partner may have a very light holding; he has made a mere one-over-one response and then returned to your first suit. As far as partner is concerned, you may have a minimum hand. You have never increased the contract. It behooves you to make one forward move at this time by bidding two no trump. Partner's next call will clarify the situation. If he persists to three clubs, you should fold up your tent and silently steal away.

10   A Small Heart. North's jump to three hearts is an attempt to shut your side out of the bidding and indicates that he has trumps and a short suit but no particular strength in high cards. In order to destroy his ruffing values, you should start leading trumps. It is better to lead the small one rather than the ace, because if your partner obtains the lead, it is desirable to retain a trump in his hand so that he can return it. However, the lead of the ace of hearts may be considered correct.

*Your score*_____

1 As dealer you hold:
♠ K J x x x ♡ A J ◇ A x x ♣ A x x
What is your opening bid? Your answer_____

2 Opponents are vulnerable. You are South and hold:
♠ x ♡ A Q x x ◇ x x x x ♣ K x x x
The bidding has proceeded:
NORTH EAST SOUTH WEST
1 ♠   2 ◇   ?
What do you bid? Your answer_____

3 As South you hold:
♠ J 10 x x x ♡ x x x ◇ x x ♣ x x x
The bidding has proceeded:
NORTH EAST SOUTH WEST
2 ♡   Pass 2 NT   Pass
3 ♡   Pass ?
What do you bid now? Your answer_____

4 Partner opens with one heart and you hold:
♠ K J x x ♡ Q J ◇ A J x x x ♣ x x
What is your response? Your answer_____

5 Opponent opens with three clubs and you hold:
♠ A K J x x ♡ Q J 10 x ◇ A K ♣ x x
What do you bid? Your answer_____

6 As South you hold:
♠ A Q ♡ Q J x ◇ x x ♣ A K Q J x x
The bidding has proceeded:
SOUTH WEST NORTH EAST
1 ♣   Pass 1 ◇   Pass
?
What do you bid now? Your answer_____

7   Partner opens with one spade and you hold:

    ♠ 10 x x x x   ♡ x   ◇ Q x   ♣ K Q 10 x x

    What do you bid?   Your answer_____

8   As South you hold:

    ♠ Q 10 x x x   ♡ A K x x   ◇ None   ♣ A K x x

    The bidding has proceeded:

SOUTH	WEST	NORTH	EAST
1 ♠	2 ◇	Pass	3 ◇
?			

    What do you bid now?   Your answer_____

9   As South you hold:

    ♠ x x x   ♡ J 10   ◇ A x x x   ♣ K Q J x

    The bidding has proceeded:

NORTH	EAST	SOUTH	WEST
1 ♡	Pass	2 ♣	Pass
2 ◇	Pass	3 ◇	Pass
3 ♡	Pass	?	

    What do you bid now?   Your answer_____

10 As West you hold:

    ♠ A Q x x   ♡ x x   ◇ K 10 x   ♣ Q J 9 x

    The bidding has proceeded:

SOUTH	WEST	NORTH	EAST
1 ♡	Pass	2 ♡	Pass
4 ♡	Pass	Pass	Pass

    What is your opening lead?   Your answer_____

ANSWERS

1   While it is acceptable to open this hand with a bid of one spade, it seems to me it is better strategy to open with one no trump, despite the holding of a five-card major suit. The hand is evenly balanced and contains a point count of 17 so that if partner fails to raise, you may be reasonably sure that no game will be missed. An opening bid of one spade may result in an awkward dilemma if partner responds with one no trump. If you pass, you

may miss a game; if you bid again, you may find yourself overboard. Take only half credit if you opened with one spade.

2   Double. Your hand has a fair prospect of developing at least four tricks against the diamond bid. Partner may reasonably be expected to develop three, which spells a two-trick set, more than the value of any game you might be able to make. There is the further consideration that you have no good prospect of playing the hand yourself because it may be a decided misfit. If your answer was two hearts, how would you feel when partner's next bid was two spades, which is very probable? A double for penalties is strongly recommended.

3   Four Hearts. This bid does not indicate any strength, it merely denotes normal trump support for the rebid heart suit. You have already denied strength by your two-no-trump response. It would be completely pointless to show the spade suit. Nothing could be gained by it and confusion might result.

4   Two Diamonds. A response of one spade because it is cheap would not be good tactics. This is a good hand opposite an opening bid of one heart and you should arrange to show both suits in their logical order, so that partner will know you have five diamonds and four spades. If your hand were weaker and you could not afford to show both suits, the response of one spade would be in order. Take five points if your response was one spade.

5   You should take the same type of action as you would have had the bidding been opened with one club, that is, a take-out double. As in all take-out doubles, partner has the option of leaving it in if he thinks it will be more profitable to do so. There is no need for you to guess what suit to bid. Partner might be short in spades and have some length in hearts. Take only three points if your bid was three spades.

6   Three No Trump. While you actually have but 19 high-card points for your bid instead of the 21 points which

are expected, the fifth and sixth clubs in your hand are certain winners and you have an excellent chance to make your contract opposite the most meager holding from partner. It would be an indiscretion to bid but two no trump, for this bid is not forcing and partner might be inclined to pass.

7   This is the type of hand for a pre-emptive raise. You have great playing strength, but no defense. Bid four spades. A temporary bid of two clubs would be poor strategy because it allows the opponents to come in cheaply and perhaps push you beyond your level. Give yourself three points if your response was two clubs and no points if you bid but two spades.

8   Despite partner's silence you should make a decided effort to move forward. The proper procedure is to double. This is still intended for a take-out, inasmuch as partner has not yet bid. Such action takes care of all contingencies. If partner has diamond strength and chooses to leave the double in, you should not find it unpleasant. If partner responds in hearts, you will bid game in that suit, and if he returns to spades, you may try for game in that suit if you feel so inclined. Charge yourself one demerit if you cue bid four diamonds. Such a call is a one-way action, and leaves partner no choice in making a decision.

9   Partner has asked you to proceed to game even though you have previously refused to support hearts. He must therefore have a very good trump suit and your support is sufficient. Raise to four hearts, instead of trying for an eleven-trick game. Take only half credit if you bid four diamonds.

10 A Heart. This is the type of bidding on which trump leads are effective, because dummy will have distribution rather than high cards. The queen of clubs is a poor second choice which is awarded only three points.

*Your score*_____

1 As South you hold:
   ♠ A K x x   ♡ A x x   ◇ x x x   ♣ x x x
   The bidding has proceeded:

SOUTH	WEST	NORTH	EAST
Pass	Pass	1 ◇	Pass
?			

   What do you bid now?   Your answer_____

2 You are South, both sides vulnerable, and you hold:
   ♠ J 10   ♡ Q J x x   ◇ K 10 x x   ♣ K x x
   The bidding has proceeded:

WEST	NORTH	EAST	SOUTH
1 ♠	Double	2 ♠	?

   What do you bid?   Your answer_____

3 You are South, vulnerable, opponents are not, and you
   hold:
   ♠ x x x   ♡ x x x   ◇ A Q x x x   ♣ x x
   The bidding has proceeded:

EAST	SOUTH	WEST	NORTH
Pass	Pass	1 ♡	2 ♣
Double	?		

   What do you bid now?   Your answer_____

4 As South you hold:
   ♠ 10 x x   ♡ K J x x   ◇ x x   ♣ Q J x x
   The bidding has proceeded:

NORTH	EAST	SOUTH	WEST
1 ◇	1 ♡	?	

   What do you bid?   Your answer_____

5 As South you hold:
♠ K J x   ♥ 10 x x   ♦ A 10 x x   ♣ K x x
The bidding has proceeded:

NORTH	EAST	SOUTH	WEST
1 ♣	1 ♠	?	

What do you bid?   Your answer_____

6 As South you hold:
♠ A K J x x x   ♥ K J x x x   ♦ A   ♣ x
The bidding has proceeded:

SOUTH	WEST	NORTH	EAST
1 ♠	Pass	2 ♥	Pass
?			

What do you bid now?   Your answer_____

7 As South you hold:
♠ J 10 x x x   ♥ A K x   ♦ x x x   ♣ J x
The bidding has proceeded:

NORTH	EAST	SOUTH	WEST
1 ♠	2 ♣	?	

What do you bid?   Your answer_____

8 As South you hold:
♠ A J x x   ♥ A K   ♦ K Q J x x   ♣ x x
The bidding has proceeded:

SOUTH	WEST	NORTH	EAST
1 ♦	Pass	1 ♠	Pass
?			

What do you bid now?   Your answer_____

9 As South you hold:
♠ A x x x   ♥ K 10 x x   ♦ K x x x   ♣ x
The bidding has proceeded:

WEST	NORTH	EAST	SOUTH
1 ♣	Double	3 ♣	?

What do you bid?   Your answer_____

10　As West you hold:
　　♠ K Q x x　♡ x　◊ A J x x　♣ K Q x x
　　The bidding has proceeded:

EAST	SOUTH	WEST	NORTH
1 ♡	2 ♣	Double	Pass
Pass	Pass		

　　What is your opening lead?　　　　　　Your answer＿＿＿＿

ANSWERS

1　One Spade. Even though you have passed a hand containing three honor tricks, it is by no means assured that your side can go to game, and you should content yourself with a mere one-over-one response in spades. If partner takes no further action, it is extremely doubtful that you will have missed a game. Your hand is of mediocre strength and will probably produce only three tricks in the play of the hand. You have a point count of only 11, distinctly short of an opening bid.

2　Opposite a partner who has doubled, this should be regarded as a good hand, and a free bid of three hearts is clearly indicated. Don't permit East's obstructive bid to deprive you of your franchise. Take half credit if you bid three diamonds.

3　Pass. You should not be alarmed by the double. Possession of two trumps and an ace should insure that no disaster will overtake you. A rescue to two diamonds would indicate either that you are victim of some type of neurosis or that you have a desire to offer partner an open affront.

4　You haven't enough for a penalty double, and your hand is not good enough for a free bid of one no trump, which denotes a good hand. If partner cannot act again, you will not have missed anything. Pass. Take three points for a one-no-trump response and no credit for a penalty double.

5　This is a good hand and there is a fair chance for game

at no trump if partner has slightly more than a minimum. However, you must not bid two no trump immediately because that would force partner to game even with an absolute minimum. Your proper call is one no trump. When this bid is made freely it denotes a good hand and partner should not pass unless he has nothing more than an opening bid. You have a point count of only 11, that is, two less than what is regarded to insist upon game.

6 The only real point of interest here is how many aces partner holds. If he has two, you should contract for a grand slam; if he has one, you should bid a small slam; and even if he has none, the hand will be safe for five hearts. Therefore, a four-no-trump bid is in order. A sudden leap from a suit to four no trump is construed as a Blackwood call.

7 Don't permit the fifth spade to get you off balance. Your hand is not rich in playing strength and a free bid of two spades adequately describes your holding. If partner has a minimum hand, there will be no game. If he has more, he should respect your free raise and bid again. A bid of four spades might work out and receives three points as a consolation prize.

8 You have a close choice between jumping to game in spades or making a false jump shift to three hearts, forcing to game. Our choice is with the former call. This hand is not suitable for Blackwood because of the two small clubs. If partner has one ace, it may be the ace of diamonds and you would be subject to the immediate loss of two club tricks. Take eight points if your bid was three hearts.

9 Your hand is the equal of an opening bid in support of one of the remaining suits and since partner has shown good values by his take-out double, you should insist upon game. If you elect to bid three in one of your suits, you risk partner's passing, or worse, raising to game with only three trumps. This hazard can be avoided by making a cue bid of four clubs. This will compel him to choose the suit best adapted to a game contract.

10 The King of Spades, despite the fact that your partner
    has bid hearts. The singleton should not be opened, be-
    cause you are not anxious to ruff. It is better to build up
    your side trick and possibly force declarer. If ruffs be-
    come desirable, you may lead the heart later. Take only
    half credit for a heart lead.

*Your score*_____

1 Your partner has opened with one heart. You hold:
♠ A Q 10 x ♡ x ◇ A Q x x x ♣ Q x x
What is your response? Your answer_____

2 Partner opens with four spades. You hold:
♠ A x x x x ♡ A x x x ◇ None ♣ Q x x
What do you bid? Your answer_____

3 As South you hold:
♠ 10 x x x ♡ K Q ◇ K x x ♣ A J x x
The bidding has proceeded:

SOUTH	WEST	NORTH	EAST
Pass	Pass	1 ♠	Pass
3 ♠	Pass	4 ♣	Pass
?			

What do you bid now? Your answer_____

4 As South you hold:
♠ A J x x ♡ x x ◇ A K Q x ♣ K Q x
The bidding has proceeded:

SOUTH	WEST	NORTH	EAST
1 ◇	Pass	1 ♠	Pass
4 ♠	Pass	4 NT	Pass
5 ♡	Pass	5 ♠	Pass
?			

What do you bid now? Your answer_____

5 As South you hold:
♠ x x ♡ A J x x x ◇ A K x ♣ x x x
The bidding has proceeded:

SOUTH	WEST	NORTH	EAST
1 ♡	Pass	1 ♠	Pass
2 ♡	Pass	2 NT	Pass
?			

What do you bid now? Your answer_____

6   As South you hold:
    ♠ x x   ♡ A K 10 x x   ◇ A x x   ♣ x x x
    The bidding has proceeded:
    SOUTH   WEST   NORTH   EAST
    1 ♡   Pass   2 NT   Pass
    ?
    What do you bid now?   Your answer_____

7   As South you hold:
    ♠ A   ♡ x   ◇ K Q J x x x   ♣ K Q J x x
    The bidding has proceeded:
    NORTH   EAST   SOUTH   WEST
    1 ◇   Pass   ?
    What do you bid?   Your answer_____

8   As South you hold:
    ♠ x x x   ♡ Q x x   ◇ K 10 x x   ♣ K J x
    The bidding has proceeded:
    WEST   NORTH   EAST   SOUTH
    1 ♣   Double Pass   ?
    What do you bid?   Your answer_____

9   As South you hold:
    ♠ A   ♡ 10 x x x   ◇ K 10 x x   ♣ K J x x
    The bidding has proceeded:
    WEST   NORTH   EAST   SOUTH
    1 ♠   Double 2 ♠   ?
    What do you bid?   Your answer_____

10 As West you hold:
    ♠ A x   ♡ x x x x   ◇ J 10 x   ♣ J 10 x x
    The bidding has proceeded:
    SOUTH   WEST   NORTH   EAST
    1 ♠   Pass   3 ♡   Pass
    4 ♡   Pass   4 ♠   Pass
    6 ♠   Pass   Pass   Pass
    What is your opening lead?   Your answer_____

ANSWERS

1   The good old-fashioned bid of two diamonds is the only correct answer. Some players have unsoundly adopted the practice of responding with one spade on this type of holding, on the ground that it is the cheapest response. Why should anyone so well provided with earthly goods be interested in seeking bargains? There is little doubt that you will eventually reach a game contract, inasmuch as your hand is better than an opening bid facing an opening bid. There is no advantage in making a response at the one level, for it is your intention to show both suits and if you bid diamonds first and spades later, opener will be aware that you have five diamonds and four spades and will be able to act accordingly.

2   Before contemplating any action that may result in impairment of the bankroll, consider that partner has announced a hand that has less than the high-card requirements for an opening bid. Presumably two honor tricks constitute his maximum. While I am willing to concede that partner may have a very special hand on which a slam might be made, a hand containing a singleton heart and the king and jack of clubs, for example, nevertheless the odds against a slam are so distinct that a pass is indicated.

3   Partner appears to be fishing around for a slam with full knowledge that you were unable to open the bidding. This is just about as fine as anyone could expect from a passing partner and you should be pleased to co-operate by bidding five clubs.

4   Pass. According to the terms of the Blackwood Convention you have no right to exercise your own opinion, even though you have a very fine hand with perhaps something to spare. When the four-no-trump bidder asks for aces, his partner must abide by the four-no-trump bidder's decision. If he is bidding properly, the opponents

have two aces. In other words, he says, "If you do not have three aces, partner, we have no slam."

5 Having fully described the strength and character of your hand, there is no further action that you should take. A non-jump rebid of two no trump by responder is not forcing. It merely invites opener to proceed to game if he has slight undisclosed values. In this case you have an absolute rock-bottom minimum and should speak again only when partner's bids are forcing.

6 Three No Trump. Responder's jump take-out to two no trump is forcing to game. This differs from the previous example, where responder's two no trump bid did not come as a jump and was merely a forward step. Take only half credit if your bid was three hearts. With a balanced hand of the no-trump family, five-card suits should not be rebid. It behooves you to seek the shorter road to game with this minimum hand.

7 Four No Trump. This is a clear-cut Blackwood bid and is appropriate because the only thing that concerns you is the number of aces held by partner and it doesn't matter which aces they are.

8 The proper response is one no trump. This is a good hand opposite a double, and the no-trump response is preferable to showing the minor suit. Had your suit been hearts or spades, preference should be given to the major. This hand contains 9 points, which makes it rank as a good hand, sufficiently strong to respond to the double with one no trump.

9 Three Spades—A cue bid which is forcing to game and which asks partner to select the suit. This action suggests that you are equally prepared for any of the unbid suits. Your hand contains 11 points in high cards and when allowance is made for the distributional advantage, that is, the singleton and three four-card suits, the hand has a real value of at least 13 points, which makes game a certainty.

10 A Small Heart. The dummy probably has five hearts be-

cause of the jump shift. The declarer certainly has three hearts, having supported that suit. Therefore, your partner may have at most a singleton. You intend to take the first trump trick and continue with another heart.

*Your score*_____

QUIZ 21

1 As dealer you hold:
   ♠ J x x x   ♡ J x x x   ◇ A K Q   ♣ K x
   What is your opening bid?   Your answer_____

2 As South you hold:
   ♠ A K Q x x   ♡ Q x x x x   ◇ Q x   ♣ J
   The bidding has proceeded:
   WEST   NORTH   EAST   SOUTH
   1 ♣   1 ◇   Pass   ?
   What do you bid?   Your answer_____

3 As South you hold:
   ♠ A 10 9 x x   ♡ J x x x   ◇ A J x   ♣ x
   The bidding has proceeded:
   WEST   NORTH   EAST   SOUTH
   1 ♣   Double   Pass   ?
   What do you bid?   Your answer_____

4 As dealer you hold:
   ♠ J x x x x   ♡ x   ◇ A 10 x   ♣ A K J x
   What is your opening bid?   Your answer_____

5 As South you hold:
   ♠ A Q J 10 x   ♡ x x   ◇ A K Q   ♣ Q x x
   The bidding has proceeded:
   SOUTH   WEST   NORTH   EAST
   1 ♠   Pass   2 ♣   Pass
   ?
   What do you bid now?   Your answer_____

6 As South you hold:
   ♠ J x ♡ J x x ◇ A x x ♣ A J 10 x x
   The bidding has proceeded:

NORTH	EAST	SOUTH	WEST
1 ♠	Pass	2 ♣	Pass
2 ♠	Pass	2 NT	Pass
3 ♡	Pass	?	

   What do you bid now?   Your answer_____

7 As South you hold:
   ♠ x x ♡ Q x x x x ◇ 10 x x ♣ K x x
   The bidding has proceeded:

WEST	NORTH	EAST	SOUTH
1 ♠	Double	2 ♠	Pass
Pass	Double	Pass	?

   What do you bid now?   Your answer_____

8 As South you hold:
   ♠ A J x x x ♡ None ◇ 10 x ♣ A J x x x x
   The bidding has proceeded:

SOUTH	WEST	NORTH	EAST
1 ♣	1 ♡	2 ◇	Pass
2 ♠	Pass	3 ◇	Pass
?			

   What do you bid now?   Your answer_____

9 As South you hold:
   ♠ J x ♡ A K 10 x x ◇ A K x x ♣ x x
   The bidding has proceeded:

SOUTH	WEST	NORTH	EAST
1 ♡	Pass	1 ♠	Pass
2 ◇	Pass	2 ♠	Pass
?			

   What do you bid now?   Your answer_____

10 As West you hold:
   ♠ 64   ♡ 97643   ◇ A75   ♣ Q94
   The bidding has proceeded:

SOUTH	WEST	NORTH	EAST
1 ♠	Pass	3 ♡	Pass
4 ♡	Pass	4 ♠	Pass
5 ♠	Pass	6 ♠	Pass
Pass	Pass		

   What is your opening lead?   Your answer_____

ANSWERS

1 One Diamond. This hand is a mandatory opening bid, as
   it contains 14 points. However, neither of the major suits
   is biddable. We will occasionally stretch a point and make
   a one-over-one response with a suit this weak, but opening bids with major suits of this character are not pre-
   scribed. We would prefer, therefore, to open with a bid
   of one diamond and hope that no complications set in.
   It is not our practice to open with two-card suits even
   though a club opening is frequently more convenient than
   a diamond.

2 With this inviting distribution we would urge a game contract, even though partner has shown no great strength
   by his overcall at the level of one. Only a call of two
   spades will be accepted as proper. A mere bid of one
   spade would not be forcing on North, who did not open
   the bidding and might decide to quit. If you choose to
   make a game-forcing bid of two clubs, we would not look
   upon it with disdain. In fact, we think enough of that call
   to make an award of five points.

3 An average hand opposite a take-out double will usually
   produce game, particularly where the principal strength
   is in the major suits and the distribution is highly favorable. The proper call is two spades. The cue bid of two
   clubs is a slight overbid and is therefore awarded only
   half credit.

4   One Club. The high-card values combined with the distributional factors of this hand make it a mandatory opening bid. The problem revolves merely around the choice of suits. Normally the longer of two biddable suits is selected for the opening, but this is subject to the rule which I have held forth for some time, namely, that all weak five-card suits should be looked upon as four-card suits for the purpose of opening the bidding. If the spade suit is regarded as a four-spade suit, the proper opening bid is one club, which is our choice. This makes the second bid so much easier. If partner responds one heart, you rebid one spade. Take only half credit if your opening bid was one spade.

5   Three Spades. You have a winning capacity of more than seven tricks plus high-card strength in excess of your opening bid. This calls for a jump rebid of some kind and the only suitable manner in which to jump is by rebidding the spades. With this nearly solid suit you are prepared to play the hand with only two trumps from partner, if he should decide to raise you with such holding. A raise to three clubs has some merit and is awarded six points.

6   Partner has shown a holding of six spades and only four hearts; you should, therefore, return to three spades, since the partnership has eight of that suit compared with only seven hearts. If partner had five spades and four hearts, he would no doubt have shown the hearts on the second round instead of rebidding spades.

7   Four Hearts. Partner has shown that he has a very sound double by forcing you to bid at the level of three despite the fact that you have declined a previous opportunity to speak. Actually, you have a fairly good hand, one with which you could not have been severely criticized for competing on the first round. The recommended bid, therefore, is four hearts. It must be borne in mind that if your response is only three hearts, partner must be prepared for your having an absolute blank, without the queen of hearts. Since partner is willing to assume the

risk of a nine-trick contract though you may have nothing, your surprise values should induce you to bid one more.

8   Three Spades. Despite the fact that partner has merely rebid his diamonds, it has been established that he has a good hand, inasmuch as he made a voluntary bid over the adverse call of one heart. His action was the more drastic in that his suit was higher in rank than yours and propels the bidding to a dangerous level. From the previous bids it is clear that North expects you to take further action, and the recommended bid is three spades, describing a five-card suit. Up to this point partner must labor under the impression that your spade suit is only four cards long, inasmuch as clubs were bid first. The rebid should clarify this and make his next decision simpler. Take only half credit if your bid was four diamonds.

9   Partner must have a good spade suit to repeat it in the face of an announced two-suiter by you. Since you have considerably more than an opening bid, you should give him one more chance by raising to three spades. Take only half credit for a bid of three hearts.

10   A Heart. Partner is probably void because North's jump to three hearts indicates that he probably holds five of the suit. South's raise to four definitely marks him with at least three. When partner ruffs the opening lead, he may not know how to return to your hand. Therefore, under the suit preference contention, you should lead the nine of hearts, which is clearly marked as an abnormal lead, inasmuch as it cannot be the fourth best and cannot be a short-suit lead. The lead of an abnormally high card calls for partner to return the higher ranking of the two remaining suits. In this way partner can reach your hand and obtain another ruff, thus defeating the contract two tricks.

*Your score*_____

97

1   As South you hold:
    ♠ A x x x   ♡ A 10 x   ◇ A K x   ♣ A 10 x
    What is your opening bid?   Your answer_____

2   As South you hold:
    ♠ A x   ♡ A 10 9 x x x   ◇ Q x   ♣ A K x
    The bidding has proceeded:

SOUTH	WEST	NORTH	EAST
1 ♡	Pass	1 ♠	Pass
?			

    What do you bid now?   Your answer_____

3   Partner opens with one spade. You hold:
    ♠ A Q x x x x   ♡ x x x   ◇ x   ♣ x x x
    What is your response?   Your answer_____

4   As South you hold:
    ♠ K Q x x x x   ♡ A K x x   ◇ Q x   ♣ x
    The bidding has proceeded:

SOUTH	WEST	NORTH	EAST
1 ♠	Pass	2 ♣	Pass
2 ♠	Pass	3 ◇	Pass
?			

    What do you bid now?   Your answer_____

5   Partner opens with one heart. You hold:
    ♠ A x x   ♡ J 10 x x   ◇ K Q   ♣ J x x x
    What is your response?   Your answer_____

6   As South you hold:
    ♠ 10 x x   ♡ K J x x x   ◇ A Q 10 x   ♣ x
    The bidding has proceeded:

NORTH	EAST	SOUTH	WEST
2 ♠	Pass	3 ♡	Pass
3 ♠	Pass	?	

    What do you bid now?   Your answer_____

7 Partner has opened with one spade. You hold:
   ♠ A 10 x ♡ 10 x x ◇ K 10 x x ♣ K x x
   What is your response?   Your answer_____

8 As South you hold:
   ♠ None ♡ A x x ◇ K J x x ♣ J x x x x
   The bidding has proceeded:
   EAST SOUTH WEST NORTH
   Pass Pass   Pass 1 ♣
   1 ♠   ?
   What do you bid now?   Your answer_____

9 As South you hold:
   ♠ A x x ♡ Q x x ◇ A 10 x x x ♣ K x
   The bidding has proceeded:
   SOUTH WEST NORTH EAST
   1 ◇   1 ♠   2 ♡   2 ♠
   Pass   Pass 4 ♣   Pass
   ?
   What do you bid now?   Your answer_____

10 As West you hold:
   ♠ K Q x x x ♡ A x ◇ x x x x ♣ x x
   The bidding has proceeded:
   SOUTH WEST NORTH EAST
   1 ♡   Pass 2 ◇   Pass
   4 ◇.   Pass 4 ♠   Pass
   5 ♣   Pass 5 ♠   Pass
   6 ♡   Pass Pass   Pass
   What is your opening lead?   Your answer_____

ANSWERS

1 One Club. This hand is too big for a bid of one no trump,
   since it contains five honor tricks and a point count of
   20. But it is not strong enough for an opening bid of two
   no trump, which would require 22 points. The suggested
   bid is one club, rather than one spade. This is done in
   order to make it easy for partner to respond if he has a

mild hand with one of the red suits, which he might chance to show at the level of one, but would not be willing to bid at the level of two.

2 Inasmuch as your hand has seven playing tricks, a strong bid is indicated and the obvious jump to three hearts is the approved procedure. Even two small hearts in partner's hand will be sufficient to make the suit a playable trump.

3 Our choice is for a pre-emptive raise to four spades. If partner has a suitable hand, he may be able to make it. If not, no serious loss can be incurred, for in such case it is not at all improbable that the opponents could score a game if permitted to get together. This raise to game describes a hand with a great deal of trump support and some distribution, but no more than 9 high-card points. Take only half credit if your bid was but two spades.

4 The other major should be shown at this time, not with any idea that you will find enough support for that suit. Partner's showing of two suits has obviated any such possibility, but you will thus describe your six–four holding to partner who will be in a better position to judge the best final contract. Bid three hearts.

5 Two clubs. A response must be manufactured, because there is no natural bid that suits this hand. It is too good for a single raise and not good enough for a jump raise which would be forcing to game. This hand is above average in strength and calls for two bids. Responder should therefore make some response which opener is not at liberty to pass, that is to say, he must name some other suit as a temporizing measure. We suggest two clubs, with the intention of raising hearts next round. Half credit is awarded for a bid of three hearts.

6 Four Diamonds. There is little doubt that there is a slam in the hand, but the better to realize the full possibilities, it is your solemn duty to show the ace of diamonds. Partner's opening two-bid and rebid of spades has presumably fixed that suit as trump and the showing of aces is now in order. Do not make the mistake of embarking on

a Blackwood bid at this point, for even if you obtained the information about the number of aces, you would not be in good position to judge the exact trick-taking potentialities of the partnership. It is better to give information in this case rather than to ask for it. If partner chooses to lash out into a Blackwood bid, that should suit your tastes entirely. Take half credit if your bid was five or six spades.

7 Two Spades. At a quick glance it might appear that this hand is just a shade too good for a single raise, but actually it is within the limits of such a call. Hands that are distributed 4–3–3–3 are never as good as they look, and when contemplating an aggressive move, you must make a slight deduction for the possession of this evenly balanced hand as responder.

8 The only way to counteract the effect of the previous pass is to make a cue bid of two spades which is forcing for at least one round. A mere jump in clubs or the naming of a new suit would not be forcing on partner, who will no doubt recall your previous pass and may exercise his option to drop the bidding. Half credit is awarded for three clubs.

9 A constructive bid by you is in order. You have previously indicated that you had opened a minimum hand by passing over the two-spade bid, whereas you might, without having stretched violently, have offered a second-round raise of the hearts. Partner has first made a free bid and then followed by reopening with a jump shift. A mere return to four hearts would be grossly inadequate, now that the king of clubs has become promoted in value. The recommended procedure is either a cue bid of four spades or a bid of five hearts. Our own preference runs slightly to the latter.

10 A Diamond. While the lead of the king of spades is very tempting, it is probable that one of the opponents has a singleton spade. A better chance to defeat the contract is to give partner a diamond ruff. North's first take-out was to two diamonds, which indicates that he probably has at

least four. South's jump to four diamonds marks him with four of the suit, which means that partner cannot have more than one. Therefore, when West obtains the lead with the ace of trumps, partner can be given the ruff.

*Your score*___

1 Partner opens with one club and you hold:
  ♠ Q J 10 x ♡ J x x ◇ K x x x ♣ x x
  What is your response?   Your answer＿＿＿＿＿

2 As South you hold:
  ♠ x x ♡ Q x x x ◇ Q 10 x x x x ♣ x
  The bidding has proceeded:
  WEST   NORTH   EAST   SOUTH
  1 ♡   2 ♣   Pass   ?
  What do you bid?   Your answer＿＿＿＿＿

3 As South you hold:
  ♠ J x x ♡ x x ◇ A J x x ♣ K J x x
  The bidding has proceeded:
  NORTH   EAST   SOUTH   WEST
  1 ♠   Double   ?
  What do you bid?   Your answer＿＿＿＿＿

4 You are South, both sides vulnerable, and both sides have
  60 part score. You hold:
  ♠ A J x x ♡ K J x ◇ J 10 x x ♣ J x
  The bidding has proceeded:
  EAST   SOUTH   WEST   NORTH
  1 ♡   ?
  What do you bid?   Your answer＿＿＿＿＿

5 As South you hold:
  ♠ A Q 10 x x x x ♡ J x ◇ x ♣ K x x
  The bidding has proceeded:
  NORTH   EAST   SOUTH   WEST
  1 ♡   Pass   1 ♠   Pass
  3 NT   Pass   ?
  What do you bid now?   Your answer＿＿＿＿＿

6 As South you hold:
   ♠ J x x ♡ x x x ◇ K x x x ♣ Q x x
   The bidding has proceeded:

EAST	SOUTH	WEST	NORTH
Pass	Pass	1 ♣	Double
Pass	1 ◇	Pass	2 ♠
Pass	?		

   What do you bid now?   Your answer_____

7 As South you hold:
   ♠ Q J 10 x ♡ None ◇ K 10 x x ♣ A J x x x
   The bidding has proceeded:

EAST	SOUTH	WEST	NORTH
Pass	Pass	Pass	1 ◇
1 ♡	?		

   What do you bid now?   Your answer_____

8 You are South and vulnerable, opponents are not. You
   hold:
   ♠ 10 x x ♡ A x ◇ Q x x ♣ K J 10 x x
   The bidding has proceeded:

EAST	SOUTH	WEST	NORTH
1 ♡	Pass	2 ♡	2 ♠
Pass	?		

   What do you bid now?   Your answer_____

9 As South you hold:
   ♠ A Q x x x ♡ x x ◇ Q x ♣ A K x x
   The bidding has proceeded:

NORTH	EAST	SOUTH	WEST
Pass	Pass	1 ♠	Pass
2 NT	Pass	?	

   What do you bid now?   Your answer_____

10   As West you hold:
    ♠ A x   ♡ A 10 x x x x   ◇ J x x x   ♣ x
    The bidding has proceeded:

SOUTH	WEST	NORTH	EAST
1 ◇	1 ♡	2 ◇	2 ♡
2 ♠	3 ♡	3 ♠	Pass
4 ♠	Pass	Pass	Pass

    What is your opening lead?   Your answer_____

ANSWERS

1   The choice lies between one spade and one diamond, with our vote going to the latter. This is a common-sense response and is calculated to make the opener's rebid as easy as possible. If he has a secondary heart or spade suit, he may show it at the level of one. A spade response by you would make it difficult for partner to show the heart suit if he has it. The one highly improper response would be one no trump. This would make it impossible for partner to rebid at the level of one, which he might well desire to do.

2   Absolutely nothing. There is no need for panic. The safest and surest way to get out of trouble is to pass. Since partner has not been doubled, no disaster is imminent even if he is permitted to play the two-club contract. But if you rescue prematurely, complications may set in. Our policy is not to rescue an undoubled partner.

3   This is an average hand in high cards (10 points) which in conjunction with mild trump support for partner justifies a redouble, and that is our choice. Take only half credit if you passed.

4   No action at all is recommended at this point. There is no need to be desperate. Opponents have not yet contracted for game and when they do, it will be time enough to assume the role of Horatius at the bridge. Partner should first be given an opportunity to act independently without a distorted picture of the scene which action by you would paint.

105

5　Partner has opened the bidding and made a powerful jump. Your hand is the equal of an opening bid, if not in high-card values, surely in playing strength, so that a slam is in sight and we suggest a bid of five spades. Approaching the problem mathematically, we see that partner has at least 21 points and you have 10, which with a seven-card suit is usually enough to produce a slam (with normal distributions the range is 33 or 34). Full credit is also awarded to six spades.

6　Two No Trump. Partner's bid of two spades is not forcing but it is next door to it. When a player first makes a take-out double and then jumps in a new suit, he expects you to bid again unless your hand is absolutely worthless. I am not here to contend that your hand is impressive but it is by no means worthless. You might not have had the king of diamonds, you might not have had the jack of spades, and you do have a technical club stopper. The recommended call is, therefore, two no trump, with a sizable demerit for a pass. Half credit if you raised partner's spades with your even distribution.

7　Our choice is two hearts. Since partner opened in fourth position, you may rely on his having a sound opening bid. It becomes clear, therefore, that you should insist upon playing this hand for game at least. Indeed, even with a minimum hand in the North there may be an easy slam if it happens to fit well. There is no way to describe the power of your hand after a previous pass, other than a cue bid in the adverse suit, announcing first-round control of hearts and by inference a satisfaction with diamonds. Some credit should be awarded to a call of three diamonds and we offer five points for that bid.

8　Three Spades. Partner has shown a good hand by competing against two bidding opponents with a passing partner. Surely he may be relied upon to take six or seven of these tricks himself and your hand should produce at least three tricks for him. The proper call is three spades. Your trump support is adequate for a partner who has made a vulnerable overcall at the level of two and should therefore have a six-card suit or an almost solid one of five cards. A demerit for bidding three clubs which is pointless. First, partner need not bid again; second, if he does rebid three spades, you will be back where you started.

9   After partner's previous pass his jump to two no trump is not forcing, but there is no doubt that we wish nevertheless to proceed to game. However, an effort should be made to find the safest contract. The suggested call is a bid of three clubs. If partner returns to three spades, we shall go on to four. If he persists to three no trump, then surely that will be the best final contract. Take only half credit for a bid of three no trump.

10   A Small Diamond, with the intention of giving partner a ruff in that suit. South has opened the bidding with a diamond, which marks him with at least four of that suit. North's immediate free raise to two diamonds indicates that he probably has four. There is the further chance that South has five, so that East can hardly have more than one diamond. When West regains the lead with the ace of trumps, another diamond should be led.

*Your score*_____

1 Partner opens with one club. You hold:
   ♠ A Q x ♡ K J x ◇ K J x x ♣ 10 x x
   What is your response?   Your answer_____

2 As South you hold:
   ♠ K J x x x ♡ x ◇ x x x ♣ A K Q x
   The bidding has proceeded:
   SOUTH   WEST   NORTH   EAST
   1 ♠   Pass   1 NT   Pass
   ?
   What do you bid now?   Your answer_____

3 As South you have 40 part score. You hold:
   ♠ x x x ♡ x ◇ Q 10 x x x ♣ x x x x
   The bidding has proceeded:
   NORTH   EAST   SOUTH   WEST
   1 ♡   Pass   ?
   What do you bid?   Your answer_____

4 You are dealer and have a part score of 70. You hold:
   ♠ A K J 10 x x x ♡ A x x ◇ K x ♣ x
   What is your opening bid?   Your answer_____

5 As dealer you hold:
   ♠ A x ♡ Q J x ◇ A Q x x x ♣ A x x
   What is your opening bid?   Your answer_____

6 As South you hold:
   ♠ x x ♡ K J x x x x ◇ K x ♣ x x x
   The bidding has proceeded:
   NORTH   EAST   SOUTH   WEST
   2 NT   Pass   ?
   What do you bid?   Your answer_____

7 As South you hold:

♠ K J x x ♡ A K x ◇ K J x x ♣ x x

The bidding has proceeded:

SOUTH	WEST	NORTH	EAST
1 ♠	Pass	2 ♡	Pass
?			

What do you bid now?   Your answer____

8 You are South; East and West are vulnerable. You hold:

♠ A J x x x ♡ x ◇ A 10 x x ♣ 10 x x

The bidding has proceeded:

NORTH	EAST	SOUTH	WEST
1 ♡	2 ♣	?	

What do you bid?   Your answer____

9 As South you hold:

♠ x x ♡ J x ◇ x x ♣ K Q 10 x x x x

The bidding has proceeded:

NORTH	EAST	SOUTH	WEST
1 ♡	Pass	2 ♣	2 ♠
Pass	Pass	?	

What do you bid now?   Your answer____

10 As West you hold:

♠ Q x ♡ x x x ◇ A K x x ♣ Q x x x

The bidding has proceeded:

SOUTH	WEST	NORTH	EAST
1 ♠	Pass	1 NT	Pass
2 ♡	Pass	4 ♡	Pass
Pass	Pass		

What is your opening lead?   Your answer____

ANSWERS

1 Since your hand is the equal of an opening bid, you should be unwilling to settle for less than game. The recommended response, therefore, is two no trump, forcing to game. The two-no-trump response is intended to cover all those evenly balanced hands, with all suits protected,

whose point count ranges from 13 to 15 (the equal of an ordinary opening bid). This hand has 14. There is nothing to be gained by a temporizing bid of one diamond, which will involve some future bid of some number of no trumps (and you may not pick the right number later in the day). Where you are in a position to finish your own job with but one tremor of the vocal cords, you should do so. A response of two no trump fully describes your hand and leaves the rest to partner.

2   The recommended call is two clubs. Not that we have any idea of going places, for since partner has a maximum high-card count of 10 points, game may be considered out of the question. But this hand, containing two unprotected suits, one of them a singleton, is not well adapted to no-trump play. The error of rebidding spades should be avoided. Such a call has nothing to gain and much to lose. If it should prove that spades will be the superior contract, partner will be in a position to return to that suit after your two-club bid. If partner happens to be short in spades and has some length in clubs, the spade rebid would be fatal. You might as well have two shots for the price of one.

3   Call me timid if you choose, but my vote is for a pass. It is my practice to go to great lengths to keep the bidding open when an advanced part score is held, but this is going too far. Too frequently have complications set in by virtue of South's "sporting" bids of one no trump in situations such as this. Partner has received no warning and carries on the fight against the expected competition from West to his great disaster. One cannot expect always to be right in these situations, but I am persuaded that the pass will be wiser in most cases.

4   The standard rule for two demand bids should be relaxed somewhat in this situation. There is considerable likelihood that partner, even with definite values, will take no action over a one-spade bid which "puts you out," and a slam may be missed. An opening two-spade bid is

110

recommended, with the suggestion that you step lightly after that.

5   As we view it, this is a clear-cut opening bid of one no trump, based on a balanced hand containing 17 points. An opening bid of one diamond would not be sound strategy, for complications might well set in. If partner, for example, should respond with one spade, no adequate rebid would be available. The hand would not be strong enough for a jump rebid of two no trump, yet much too good for a mere one-no-trump rebid.

6   This hand stands a very good chance of producing five or six tricks for partner and, consequently, is on the verge of a slam. The best way to indicate such a holding is by a big jump in hearts. Our own preference is for five hearts. However, the situation may be handled adequately by first responding with three hearts, intending to make a leap beyond game on the next round.

7   Do not complicate matters by bidding three diamonds. You have slight values in excess of your opening bid and an immediate raise to three hearts will express them. The spade bid was selected by you for your opening bid because the hand is of moderate strength only, and the expected response was two clubs. This would make it easy to rebid two diamonds, whereas an opening bid of one diamond would have made it embarrassing to rebid over the anticipated two-club response.

8   A special demerit for bidding two spades. The fact that you have 11 points and two honor tricks opposite an opening bid is not justification for taking this dangerous action. A bid of two spades by you would be forcing for one round and would probably result in a rebid of three hearts by partner. If you are able to extricate yourself from this predicament, you have greater resourcefulness than I. I think it is safe to assume that you can win three or four tricks against the club declaration which, added to the three that the opening bidder is expected to produce, adds up to a sizable profit. If opener happens to

have a good hand, the yield may even run into four figures, so that this is a clear-cut penalty double.

9   I would be inclined to suspect that the opposition have misjudged their strength and would not be disposed to give them a chance to reconsider. Partner evidently does not have a very strong hand, for he was not in position to make a free rebid; the opposition must therefore have considerable high-card strength. It was length alone which was the basis of your first response at the level of two; you must not use the same grounds for further action which would lead partner to believe you have a strong hand. A graceful exit is therefore recommended.

10 A Trump. This does not mean that you should first lead the king of diamonds for a look at the dummy. The lead of the king of diamonds will permit declarer to make the hand. You do not need a look at the dummy to know it will be short in spades and have four hearts. Your partner probably has some good spades which you should protect by leading trump as often as possible. Keep the ace and king of diamonds to get in with, to lead more trump.

*Your score*_____

1 Partner opens with one no trump. You hold:
   ♠ xx ♡ Axxx ◇ A10xxx ♣ K10
   What is your response?   Your answer_____

2 As dealer you hold:
   ♠ AKJ10x ♡ Axx ◇ Ax ♣ AJx
   What is your opening bid?   Your answer_____

3 As South you hold:
   ♠ KQ10xx ♡ xx ◇ AQx ♣ Kxx
   The bidding has proceeded:
   SOUTH   WEST   NORTH   EAST
   1 ♠   Pass   2 ♡   Pass
   ?
   What do you bid now?   Your answer_____

4 As South you hold:
   ♠ AKxx ♡ KJxx ◇ xx ♣ Qxx
   The bidding has proceeded:
   EAST   SOUTH   WEST   NORTH
   1 ◇   Double Redouble Pass
   Pass   ?
   What do you bid now?   Your answer_____

5 Partner opens with one no trump. You hold:
   ♠ x ♡ KJxxxx ◇ K10xx ♣ xx
   What is your response?   Your answer_____

6 Both sides are vulnerable, opponent opens with one
   spade, and you hold:
   ♠ xxx ♡ AQx ◇ AKx ♣ xxxx
   What do you bid?   Your answer_____

7 You are South and have 60 part score. You hold:
♠ x ♡ K Q 10 x ♢ x x ♣ A K Q 10 x x
The bidding has proceeded:

SOUTH	WEST	NORTH	EAST
1 ♣	1 ♢	1 ♡	1 ♠
?			

What do you bid?   Your answer_____

8 Partner opens with two no trump. You hold:
♠ J x x x x ♡ K x ♢ J x ♣ K Q x x
What is your response?   Your answer_____

9 As South you hold:
♠ Q J ♡ K x x ♢ x x x ♣ A K 10 x x
The bidding has proceeded:

NORTH	EAST	SOUTH	WEST
1 ♡	Pass	2 ♣	Pass
2 ♠	Pass	?	

What do you bid now?   Your answer_____

10 As West you hold:
♠ Q ♡ A K x x ♢ A Q x x ♣ Q x x x
The bidding has proceeded:

SOUTH	WEST	NORTH	EAST
1 ♠	Double	Pass	Pass
Pass			

What is your opening lead?   Your answer_____

ANSWERS

1 Two Clubs. You have 11 points in high cards and therefore enough to raise to three no trump. Such a bid, however, would not be the best strategy, for partner might
have four hearts in which case a four-heart contract
might offer a safer play for the game. The proper response is two clubs, a bid which is conventional and asks
partner to bid a four-card major suit if he has one. If
partner rebids two diamonds, which shows no major, you
contract for three no trump. The same thing applies if

114

his rebid is two spades. On the other hand, if he rebids two hearts you will cheerfully raise to four. Three diamonds has merit in that it offers the possibility of playing four hearts (should opener rebid three), three no trump, or five diamonds, and full credit is also given for that call.

2   Two No Trump. This hand is not quite strong enough for an opening bid of two spades, which would be forcing to game, inasmuch as the hand contains at least five losers. Yet it is too strong to risk an opening bid of one spade, for partner might have as little as 4 points and refuse to keep it open. The recommended bid is two no trump, which partner may pass if he has less than 4 points. This hand counts 22, since an additional point is added to the value when all four aces are held. Take only half credit if your opening bid was two spades.

3   While all the suits are stopped, a rebid of two no trump is not recommended because the hand is not strong enough to justify such action. Very little over a minimum is held and a rebid of two spades does justice to the holding. To qualify as a sound rebid of two no trump, the opening hand should have roughly the high-card equivalent of an opening one-no-trump bid, that is to say about 15–17 points.

4   It is incumbent upon you to take action, and the suggested bid is one heart as the cheapest way of escaping from the temporarily awkward situation. Partner's pass of the one diamond redoubled should not be construed as a willingness to play at that contract. Partner in effect is saying, "Get yourself out as cheaply as possible."

5   Facing a hand that contains about four high-card tricks (at least 16 points), your holding will most probably produce four hearts, and that is the bid recommended by your host. A bid of three hearts would be improper, for that would denote more in the way of high cards. A bid of two hearts is not recommended, for partner would pass with an ordinary no trump.

6   Despite the holding of 13 high-card points, this is not the

type of hand with which to compete. The defensive possibilities are great but offensively this hand is actually feeble. There may be no safe place to play it. Pass and do not enter the auction unless the enemy stops bidding at an early stage. Remember, a 13-point hand is an optional opening bid, and since you do not have a comfortable rebid, you should choose not to exercise your option.

7   Three Hearts. Some effort should be made to reach slam, which might be readily attainable if partner has control of diamonds. This suggested call is three hearts, overbidding the game. If partner obliges by bidding three spades to show the spade control, you may now jump to five hearts. This should make it clear that everything is under control but diamonds, but if partner has second-round control of that suit, he may then contract for slam. If in response to your three-heart bid partner bids four diamonds, you may safely contract for six hearts, expecting to lose only a spade trick. Your club suit should provide discards for any of partner's losing diamonds.

8   Three Spades. In high-card strength you have sufficient to justify a slam suggestion. Your hand counts 10 and partner has a minimum of 22, which adds to within a point or two of a slam. However, with this unbalanced hand we prefer first to show the five-card suit and then follow up with a raise of the no trump if partner returns to three no trump.

9   Happy days are here. Partner has described a holding that contains five hearts and four spades, but, what is more, by bidding his suits in this order, he has advertised a strong hand, one containing the equivalent of at least four honor tricks, and about 19 points. Since he can have no more than three and a half high-card tricks in the majors, his hand could hardly contain two losing diamonds. A bid of six hearts is therefore not out of line, but a call of five hearts would hardly place the game in jeopardy and that is the call that receives our first choice. Take only half credit if your bid was three or four hearts.

10 The Queen of Spades. When your partner leaves in your take-out double of one in a suit, he announces that his trumps are good enough to defeat the contract. Therefore, you should start pulling trumps immediately.

*Your score*___

QUIZ 26

1 Partner opens with one heart. You hold:
   ♠ K x x ♡ J x x ◇ A Q x x ♣ A Q x
   What is your response?   Your answer_____

2 Partner opens with one spade. You hold:
   ♠ x x ♡ A Q J 10 x x ◇ A Q x ♣ K 10
   What is your response?   Your answer_____

3 As South you hold:
   ♠ K J 10 ♡ Q J 10 x ◇ A 10 x ♣ A x x
   The bidding has proceeded:
   WEST   NORTH   EAST   SOUTH
   1 ♡   Pass   2 ♡   ?
   What do you bid?   Your answer_____

4 As South you hold:
   ♠ A x x x ♡ K x x ◇ A K Q x x ♣ x
   The bidding has proceeded:
   EAST   SOUTH   WEST   NORTH
   1 ♣   Double Pass   1 ♡
   Pass   ?
   What do you bid now?   Your answer_____

5 As South you hold:
   ♠ K x ♡ J x x x ◇ x x x ♣ A K Q x
   The bidding has proceeded:
   NORTH   EAST   SOUTH   WEST
   1 ♠   Pass   2 ♣   Pass
   2 ♠   Pass   ?
   What do you bid now?   Your answer_____

118

6 As South you hold:
♠ A Q x x ♡ A x ◇ Q x x x x x ♣ 10
The bidding has proceeded:

SOUTH	WEST	NORTH	EAST
1 ◇	1 ♡	2 ♣	Pass
2 ◇	Pass	3 ◇	Pass
?			

What do you bid now?   Your answer_____

7 As South you hold:
♠ A K 10 x ♡ K Q x ◇ K x ♣ K Q x x
The bidding has proceeded:

SOUTH	WEST	NORTH	EAST
1 ♣	Pass	1 ◇	Pass
?			

What do you bid now?   Your answer_____

8 Both sides are vulnerable, you have 60 part score, and hold:
♠ None ♡ A K x x ◇ K Q J 10 x ♣ A Q x x
Your right-hand opponent opens with one heart.
What do you bid?   Your answer_____

9 Partner opens with one club. You hold:
♠ K Q J 10 x x x x ♡ K Q ◇ 10 ♣ K Q
What is your response?   Your answer_____

10 As West you hold:
♠ 10 x x x ♡ A Q x x ◇ x x ♣ K J x
The bidding has proceeded:

NORTH	EAST	SOUTH	WEST
1 ◇	Pass	1 ♠	Pass
3 ◇	Pass	3 ♠	Pass
4 ♠	Pass	Pass	Pass

What is your opening lead?   Your answer_____

ANSWERS

1 Three No Trump. Indirect bids are to be avoided when a direct bid will paint a precise picture of your holding. There is such a response available in the bid of three no trump, which describes a hand that is evenly balanced and contains 16 to 18 points. Do not make the mistake of responding with two no trump, which is restricted to hands counting 13 to 15. After your response of three no trump, partner will be in a position to count the exact resources of the partnership and will therefore know whether or not there is a chance for slam. A response of two diamonds is not recommended. It would simply lead to a difficult rebidding problem on subsequent rounds.

2 Our choice is for a jump shift of three hearts. The hand has distinct slam possibilities despite the lack of spade support, and therefore the immediate slam signal is recommended. Your trump suit is good enough to stand on its own merit and you can surely underwrite a game in hearts. Support for partner is not required in making a jump shift if your own suit is self-sustaining. Two hearts may lead to complications in the later stages of the auction and for that reason is awarded but five points.

3 Pass. You might as well accept a short profit. You have no reason to feel confident that you can make three of anything with this unattractive distribution, and a double by you would oblige partner to bid.

4 Two Diamonds. Inasmuch as partner has been forced to bid and may have only scant values, a jump bid is not in order. A strong hand has already been advertised by the double and the best strategy calls for a bid of only two diamonds. If partner has any values, he should make a further bid. If he happens to rebid hearts, you may then go to game in that suit. One should be reluctant to give an immediate raise with only three trumps where partner has been forced to bid. Take three points if your call was two hearts.

5   Three Spades. Your hand is virtually the equal of an opening bid. You should therefore strongly contemplate a game contract. Since partner has rebid spades, you now have normal trump support and a raise to three is recommended. There is no occasion to speculate with a doubtful no-trump bid, lacking a diamond stopper, when an entirely adequate old-fashioned bid is available in the form of a prosaic raise.

6   Three Spades. Further action by you is indicated. True enough, this hand is minimum in high-card strength, but it is by no means minimum in playing strength. Partner has shown a hand of distinct offensive strength by first making a free bid in a new suit and then raising after a minimum rebid by you. The recommended bid is three spades. If partner then returns to four diamonds, you may decide to quit, but the hand should be safe for four.

7   Two No Trump. While it is my practice to avoid suppressing major suits during the early stages of the auction, convenience dictates a departure from this policy. This is a powerful hand and a mere rebid of one spade would not do justice to the holding. The point is that the naming of a new suit by opener is not forcing. Our vote goes to a rebid of two no trump; this, too, is not forcing if partner has made a weak one-over-one take-out, but it is more likely to elicit a further bid from partner and at the same time give a full description of the type and strength of the hand (19 or 20 points).

8   My preference is for a simple overcall of two diamonds. This may seem very strange with a hand containing about five honor tricks. But a take-out double is not recommended because of the danger that partner, who may hold a long spade suit, will not subside in time if he is asked to come into the auction. The chances of missing a slam by making the simple overcall are distinctly remote, for partner would have to produce considerable trick-taking power to bring us up to twelve tricks against the vulnerable opening.

9   This is the ideal type of hand for the Blackwood Conven-

tion since the only losers are aces, and our own choice is an immediate leap to four no trump, a clear-cut Blackwood bid. If partner happens to have four aces, the grand slam is easy. If he has three, you contract for small slam. If he has only two, your contract of five spades will be safe. I will concede that in a remote case your Blackwood bid may prove disastrous, and that is where partner has chosen to open with a string of clubs headed by the ace-jack and some diamonds headed by the king-queen. However, I believe it is worth assuming that risk.

10 A Small Club. This lead is suggested because the dummy has shown a very good diamond suit, which will provide discards, unless your tricks are taken in a hurry. It is pointless to make a waiting lead when dummy has a good long suit. You must trust that your partner has either the ace or the queen of clubs. If not, in all probability there is no hope to defeat the contract.

*Your score*_____

1 Both sides vulnerable, as South you hold:
  ♠ Q x x x ♡ 10 x ◇ K Q x x x ♣ K 10
  The bidding has proceeded:

SOUTH	WEST	NORTH	EAST
Pass	Pass	1 ♠	Double
?			

  What do you bid now?   Your answer_____

2 Partner opens with one no trump. You hold:
  ♠ Q x x ♡ A x ◇ Q J 10 x x x ♣ 10 x
  What is your response?   Your answer_____

3 Partner opens with one heart. You hold:
  ♠ K Q x x x ♡ J x x x ◇ x x ♣ x x
  What is your response?   Your answer_____

4 As South you hold:
  ♠ K 10 x x ♡ x ◇ A J x x x x ♣ x x
  The bidding has proceeded:

EAST	SOUTH	WEST	NORTH
Pass	Pass	1 ♡	Double
Pass	?		

  What do you bid now?   Your answer_____

5 As South you hold:
  ♠ A Q 10 x x x ♡ A K x ◇ J x ♣ 10 x
  The bidding has proceeded:

SOUTH	WEST	NORTH	EAST
1 ♠	Pass	2 ♣	Pass
?			

  What do you bid now?   Your answer_____

6 As South you hold:
♠ x x ♡ A K 10 x x ♢ x x x ♣ K x x
The bidding has proceeded:

NORTH	EAST	SOUTH	WEST
1 ♣	Pass	1 ♡	1 ♠
1 NT	Pass	?	

What do you bid now?   Your answer_____

7 As South you hold:
♠ x x ♡ A Q x x x ♢ A Q 10 x x ♣ K
The bidding has proceeded:

NORTH	EAST	SOUTH	WEST
1 ♡	Pass	1 ♠	Pass
2 ♢	Pass	3 ♢	Pass
?			

What do you bid now?   Your answer_____

8 As South you hold:
♠ x x x ♡ K 10 ♢ A J x ♣ A K 10 x x
The bidding has proceeded:

SOUTH	WEST	NORTH	EAST
1 ♣	1 ♠	2 ♡	Pass
?			

What do you bid now?   Your answer_____

9 As South you hold:
♠ K x ♡ x x x ♢ A 10 x x x ♣ J x x
The bidding has proceeded:

NORTH	EAST	SOUTH	WEST
Pass	1 NT	Pass	Pass
Double	Pass	?	

What do you bid now?   Your answer_____

10 As West you hold:
♠ 1098 ♡ A K 10 ♢ A Q x ♣ Q 10 x x
The bidding has proceeded:

SOUTH	WEST	NORTH	EAST
1 ♠	Double	2 ♠	Pass
Pass	Pass		

What is your opening lead?   Your answer_____

124

ANSWERS

1 The indicated call is the redouble. A hand that is average in high cards (10 points) with trump support for partner qualifies as a redouble. Particularly in view of your previous pass, partner can hardly look for more than this in the way of point count. A jump to three spades is not recommended. Partner would no doubt interpret such action as an attempt to impede the opposition, rather than as a strength-showing gesture on your part.

2 You have the requisite high-card strength for a raise to two no trump, to wit, 9 points, and the raise is therefore mandatory. By all means avoid the completely pointless call of two diamonds. A take-out to two of a minor suit must never be made in response to an opening one-no-trump bid if responder has as many as 8 points. Take full credit for three no trump.

3 Two Hearts. It may be distasteful to suppress a good five-card major suit at this low level, but expediency dictates that this be done. Your hand is of only mediocre strength and you must not conduct the bidding in such a manner that your partner will gain the impression that you have a strong holding. This is apt to be the case if you bid spades and also raise hearts. The logical procedure is to offer partner a single raise in his suit, which just about describes the strength of your hand. Half credit only, if your bid was one spade.

4 This hand has game possibilities opposite a sound take-out double, and a jump bid by you is in order. The recommended call is three diamonds. A response of two diamonds would be highly unsound, for there is too great a likelihood that partner will have to pass. Two spades has some merit and is awarded half credit.

5 A mere rebid of two spades is the only suitable call available. While this is a very representative hand, it does not qualify as a jump rebid. In order to justify a three-spade rebid, opener would have to be able to win seven tricks

in his own hand and this falls short of the mark. If responder speaks again, which is rather likely, you may show animation on the next round. If partner chooses to pass, you will realize that he has no fit in spades and that game is therefore not in sight.

6   Two No Trump. Partner has announced a strong hand by making a free rebid of one no trump after the adverse spade bid. It must be borne in mind that your response at the level of one has promised very little strength. Chances for game therefore appear to be bright. The rebid of the good five-card heart suit is not recommended, for your hand is of the no-trump type. A bid of two clubs would be highly improper, for that would be a warning against no trump. The suggested call is a raise of the no trump. With a timid partner, perhaps to three no trump; with most partners a raise to two no trump would suffice. The arithmetical basis is this: you have 10 points and partner's bidding should be based upon a hand that is very close to 16.

7   Four Diamonds. Partner's one-over-one response had not promised much strength but when combined with the subsequent raise to three diamonds it designates a good hand. The three-diamond bid is highly constructive, since your two-diamond bid was not forcing on responder. Game aspirations should therefore be entertained and our choice is for a bid of four diamonds. On the values held it is nearer to a five-diamond bid, but the lesser call has this advantage, that if responder happens to have a hand containing three small hearts, he will have the opportunity to try four hearts over four diamonds, at which point you would be pleased to play the hand. A bid of three hearts over three diamonds is not our choice because partner might be induced to raise to four on some hands containing only two trumps. Take full credit if your answer was four diamonds, only half credit if your answer was five diamonds.

8   This is an awkward situation. You have a very fine hand and no entirely suitable call is available to describe the

nature of your holding. The hand is too good for a mere minimum rebid of three clubs, no trump is out of the question without spades, so that the least of evils is to raise partner to three hearts. We are normally disinclined to make an immediate raise with only two trumps, but it must be recalled that partner's free bid of two hearts was a drastic step and indicated a powerful hand. It is always a risky matter to make a free bid at the level of two in a suit that is higher in rank than partner's suit, for the bidding is automatically forced to the three level. North should therefore make allowances for a raise under pressure.

9   You have splendid defense against a no-trump contract and should pass. We have not lost sight of partner's previous pass, but in view of the fact that he was willing to double the no-trump bid, he must be just under an opening bid himself. Allowing him about 12 or 13 points, and the opening bidder about 17, it is plain to see that dummy is virtually valueless. This places quite a job on East's shoulders.

10 The Ten of Spades. It is not advisable to lead the king of hearts for a look at the dummy. The dummy will very likely have some trumps and a short suit, and the sooner you extract dummy's trumps the better.

Your score_____

1 As South you hold:
   ♠ K J 10 x ♡ A J x ◊ Q 10 x ♣ A Q x
   The bidding has proceeded:

SOUTH	WEST	NORTH	EAST
1 NT	Pass	2 NT	Pass
?			

   What do you bid now?   Your answer_____

2 As South you hold:
   ♠ A J x x ♡ Q 10 x x ◊ A x ♣ K x x
   The bidding has proceeded:

SOUTH	WEST	NORTH	EAST
1 ♠	Pass	2 ◊	Pass
?			

   What do you bid now?   Your answer_____

3 Partner opens with one heart. You hold:
   ♠ A x x x ♡ J 10 x x x ◊ x x x x ♣ None
   What is your response?   Your answer_____

4 As South you hold:
   ♠ K J x ♡ A K x x ◊ Q x ♣ x x x x
   The bidding has proceeded:

NORTH	EAST	SOUTH	WEST
1 ◊	Pass	1 ♡	Pass
3 ♡	Pass	?	

   What do you bid now?   Your answer_____

5 As South you hold:
   ♠ x x x ♡ x x x x ◊ J x ♣ A Q x x
   The bidding has proceeded:

NORTH	EAST	SOUTH	WEST
1 ♠	Pass	1 NT	Pass
2 ♡	Pass	?	

   What do you bid now?   Your answer_____

6 Partner opens with one heart and you hold:
♠ J x x x x   ♡ K x x   ♢ 10 x   ♣ A x x
What is your response?   Your answer_____

7 As South you hold:
♠ A 10 x x   ♡ J 10 x   ♢ A Q J x x x   ♣ None
The bidding has proceeded:

SOUTH	WEST	NORTH	EAST
1 ♢	Pass	1 ♡	Pass
?			

What do you bid now?   Your answer_____

8 As South you hold:
♠ 10 x x x   ♡ A K x x   ♢ x   ♣ x x x x
The bidding has proceeded:

WEST	NORTH	EAST	SOUTH
1 ♢	Double	Pass	1 ♡
Pass	1 ♠	Pass	?

What do you bid now?   Your answer_____

9 As South you hold:
♠ K J x x x   ♡ None   ♢ K x   ♣ A Q x x x x
The bidding has proceeded:

SOUTH	WEST	NORTH	EAST
1 ♣	Pass	1 ♡	Pass
1 ♠	Pass	2 NT	Pass
3 ♠	Pass	4 ♠	Pass
?			

What do you bid now?   Your answer_____

10 As West you hold:
♠ x x   ♡ A x x   ♢ J x x x   ♣ Q x x x
The bidding has proceeded:

SOUTH	WEST	NORTH	EAST
1 ♠	Pass	2 NT	Pass
3 ♠	Pass	4 ♠	Pass
Pass	Pass		

What is your opening lead?   Your answer_____

ANSWERS

1 Three Spades. Since you have more than a minimum no
trump, it is your intention to proceed to game. Instead of
contracting for three no trump in routine fashion, it is
suggested that you afford yourself an additional chance
with no further cost by trying three spades. If it should
develop that partner's raise has been based on a hand
containing four spades and some worthless doubleton, the
major suit will very likely provide a superior contract
and partner will raise to four. In the absence of such
holding, he is duty-bound to proceed to three no trump,
and nothing will have been lost by your inquiry. Half
credit only, if your bid was three no trump.

2 Two Hearts. This is not much more than a minimum
opening bid and that rebid should be chosen which will
not give partner an impression of strength. Resist, therefore, the temptation to bid two no trump. Such a call
describes a stronger hand than this. The suggested rebid
is two hearts. This is a less expensive call and permits
partner to return to two spades if he chooses. A rebid of
two no trump would make it impossible to return to two
spades and is therefore a more drastic form of action.

3 Four Hearts. With hands of this type it is not usually
profitable to dilly-dally. You have not much in the way
of defense against the opposition should they start competing and you have great playing strength for partner.
This pre-emptive raise announces great strength in trumps
and favorable distribution, but not much in high-card
strength.

4 My old formula applies in this case. You have an opening bid facing a partner who has opened and jumped,
which suggests a slam. There is the further consideration
that the queen of diamonds is promoted in value by reason of partner's bid in that suit. The suggested bid is five
hearts. Partner should realize as a result of such action

that you have a very fine hand but no side ace to show.

5   Pass. In absence of deep reflection there may be a temptation to raise, but my vote goes against such action. In a remote case a game might be lost by such pass, but in a vast majority of holdings, points will be saved by permitting partner to play at two hearts. You have only a jack above the minimum requirement for your original no-trump response, which requires 6 points at least, and you have but 7. It is well to recall that partner's hand cannot be very powerful or it would have been his place to jump the bid on the second round. Visualize him for example with:

♠ A K x x x   ♡ A K x x   ◇ x x   ♣ x x

He will surely proceed if you raise, and there will be no play for game and a splendid chance of being set at three hearts.

6   This is a mediocre hand and you can afford to make only one forward bid, consequently the proper response is two hearts. A bid of one spade would be a tactical error because you will be in a position where you cannot also support hearts with safety. When you are not in a position to do both, the raise of partner's major suit should be preferred.

7   The suggested bid is one spade. There are several choices which include rebidding diamonds and supporting hearts. The hand is too strong for a mere two-diamond rebid, and not quite strong enough for a jump to three diamonds, so that the choice narrows down. While the bid of one spade is not forcing, partner will nevertheless in these circumstances exert every effort to speak again and a better idea of the contents of his hand may be obtained from his next move.

8   A jump by you is in order. Holding 10 points in support of spades, you should visualize game probabilities, and a single raise in spades would not do justice to your hand. Three spades is therefore the recommended bid.

9   Pass. You have already done your full duty by this hand

and should not be unduly influenced by the distributional features which you have already described. Your hand is quite minimum as to high cards and you may assume that partner is on guard that you may have a six–five distribution. His response of one heart has done nothing to improve your hand and any slam suggestion should come from him if there is to be a sound play for it.

10 A Small Heart. This is one of the rare cases in which the underlead of an ace is recommended. You have no attractive lead. The dummy has bid two no trump and surely he has the king of hearts, and your lead may deceive the declarer into misguessing.

*Your score*_____

1   As South you hold:
    ♠ 10 x   ♡ x x   ◇ A K Q x x x x   ♣ x x
    The bidding has proceeded:

EAST	SOUTH	WEST	NORTH
1 ♡	2 ◇	Pass	2 NT
Pass	?		

    What do you bid now?   Your answer_____

2   Partner opens with one club and you hold:
    ♠ J x x x   ♡ Q x x x   ◇ Q 10 x x   ♣ x
    What is your response?   Your answer_____

3   Partner opens with one club. You hold:
    ♠ K x x x   ♡ K x x   ◇ A K x x   ♣ J x
    What is your response?   Your answer_____

4   As South you hold:
    ♠ A K x x x   ♡ K   ◇ J x x x   ♣ A K Q
    The bidding has proceeded:

SOUTH	WEST	NORTH	EAST
1 ♠	Pass	1 NT	Pass
?			

    What do you bid now?   Your answer_____

5   As South you hold:
    ♠ A Q J x   ♡ A 10 x   ◇ A K Q x x   ♣ x
    The bidding has proceeded:

SOUTH	WEST	NORTH	EAST
1 ◇	Pass	1 ♡	Pass
?			

    What do you bid now?   Your answer_____

6   As South you hold:
    ♠ 10 x x   ♡ A x x x   ◇ A K x x   ♣ Q x
    The bidding has proceeded:

NORTH	EAST	SOUTH	WEST
1 ♣	Pass	1 ♡	Pass
2 ♣	Pass	2 ◇	Pass
3 ♣	Pass	?	

    What do you bid now?   Your answer_____

7   As South you hold:
    ♠ x x   ♡ K 10 x x   ◇ J 10 x   ♣ K J x x
    The bidding has proceeded:

NORTH	EAST	SOUTH	WEST
1 ♠	Pass	1 NT	Pass
2 ♡	Pass	?	

    What do you bid now?   Your answer_____

8   As South you hold:
    ♠ A K Q x x   ♡ A J x x x   ◇ Q   ♣ Q x
    The bidding has proceeded:

SOUTH	WEST	NORTH	EAST
1 ♠	Pass	2 ♣	Pass
2 ♡	Pass	3 ♣	Pass
?			

    What do you bid now?   Your answer_____

9   As South you hold:
    ♠ x   ♡ A 10 x x   ◇ x x   ♣ K Q 10 x x x
    The bidding has proceeded:

WEST	NORTH	EAST	SOUTH
3 ♠	4 ♠	Pass	?

    What do you bid?   Your answer_____

10 As West you hold:
    ♠ x   ♡ Q 10 x x   ◇ K x x   ♣ K Q J x x
    The bidding has proceeded:

NORTH	EAST	SOUTH	WEST
1 ◇	1 ♠	2 ♡	Pass
3 ♡	Pass	Pass	Pass

    What is your opening lead?   Your answer_____

134

ANSWERS

1   Your partner is behaving in a most decorous manner and your appreciation of his efforts should be manifested by a raise to three no trump. You can contribute seven tricks to the cause and it would be strange indeed if partner could not help along with two in view of the fact that he acted without your solicitation. Your hand is the perfect type of dummy for a no-trump contract. If your answer was three diamonds or, for that matter, any number of diamonds, you may hide your blushes in the nearest corner.

2   One Diamond. This hand does not contain the 6 points that are technically required for a response, but we are disinclined to pass partner out in a bid of one club where there is any reasonable excuse for bidding. Partner may have a second suit consisting of hearts or spades, and a better result will be obtained if he is afforded the opportunity to show it. A one-diamond response allows for this contingency. The worst possible procedure would be to bid one no trump. It would be better to pass.

3   Inasmuch as your hand is the equal of an opening bid, it is your purpose to reach a game contract. You have the necessary values (14 points) for a two-no-trump response and such a call is acceptable. My own preference, however, is for a temporizing bid of one diamond, to afford partner the opportunity to show a mild four-card spade suit at the level of one. In that case, I would vigorously support the major. If the small spade were a club, the only acceptable response would be two no trump.

4   I would not be inclined to play for less than game and would proceed forthwith to three no trump. This hand contains 20 points. Partner, who has responded with one no trump, may be relied upon for at least 6. The singleton heart should not be a deterrent, for it is an impressive singleton and partner almost certainly has values in that

suit. A raise to two no trump would be accepted but is awarded only five points. No credit would be allowed for a rebid of two spades.

5 You should insist upon reaching game and this may properly be done only by making a jump shift, that is to say, two spades. A rebid of only one spade would not be forcing. It should be recalled that the naming of a new suit does not force responder to bid again. A jump to three hearts would not be acceptable for two reasons: one is the lack of a fourth trump, and the other is that such a bid is not forcing upon the person who did not open the bidding.

6 Four Clubs. Since you have better than an opening bid, you should make one more try for game. It is true that partner has twice signed off, but that does not alter the fact that he still retains his opening bid. Your hand is more than an opening bid when one regards the queen of clubs as a sure winner, and recommended bid is four clubs. This still affords partner the option of checking out if he happens to be sorry about it all. It is hard to visualize a hand on which a ten-trick contract would not be safe on this sequence of bids. Take no credit if your bid was three no trump.

7 Our vote is in favor of a bid of three hearts, but it is a close decision and no criticism should attend a pass. Our preference is to bid because, while it is true that on a certain number of hands we might be in jeopardy at three hearts or that partner might proceed to game with no good play for the contract, nevertheless it is worth the risk because of the occasional game that will be unearthed in this manner. Remember, too, that partner need not go on, inasmuch as you have previously notified him that you were no ball of fire. Your hand contains 8 high-card points, which is a near maximum for a one-no-trump response. Then, too, the king of hearts is promoted to four points, which gives you a total of 10 points in support of hearts.

8   Our choice is a bid of four clubs. Partner must have a
    very substantial suit to insist upon it in the face of your
    showing a major two-suiter. A rebid of three hearts might
    tend to make partner lose interest since it would sound
    merely like an effort on your part to force him into show-
    ing a preference, which he has once refused to do. A re-
    bid of three spades would be somewhat more aggressive,
    but the support of the clubs is bound to paint a better
    picture of your holding. Take only half credit if your re-
    bid was three hearts.

9   Partner has forced you to bid at the level of five despite
    the fact that you may have nothing. With any type of
    club suit, you would have been obliged to bid five clubs;
    with this great amount of unexpected strength, you should
    indicate it by bidding six clubs. In fact, a bid of seven
    would be closer to the truth than a bid of only five.

10 The King of Clubs. Your trump holding is so strong that
    you do not desire to obtain spade ruffs. You are more
    interested in forcing the declarer, and the club suit offers
    a very bright prospect of establishing that force. If sub-
    sequent developments show that ruffs are required, you
    can always lead the spade later.

*Your score*_____

1 As South you hold:
   ♠ K 10 x   ♡ Q J x   ◊ A K x x x   ♣ K x
   The bidding has proceeded:

SOUTH	WEST	NORTH	EAST
1 ◊	Pass	1 ♡	Pass
?			

   What do you bid now?   Your answer_____

2 As South you hold:
   ♠ K J x x x x   ♡ Q x x   ◊ None   ♣ A Q J x
   The bidding has proceeded:

SOUTH	WEST	NORTH	EAST
1 ♠	Pass	1 NT	Pass
?			

   What do you bid now?   Your answer_____

3 As South you hold:
   ♠ A K Q J x x   ♡ K x x x   ◊ x x   ♣ x
   The bidding has proceeded:

SOUTH	WEST	NORTH	EAST
1 ♠	Pass	3 NT	Pass
?			

   What do you bid now?   Your answer_____

4 As South you hold:
   ♠ Q x x x x   ♡ Q   ◊ 10 x   ♣ Q 10 x x x
   The bidding has proceeded:

NORTH	EAST	SOUTH	WEST
2 ♠	Pass	2 NT	Pass
3 NT	Pass	?	

   What do you bid now?   Your answer_____

5 As South you hold:
   ♠ KJxxx ♡ None ◇ KQxx ♣ Qxxx
   The bidding has proceeded:

   SOUTH   WEST   NORTH   EAST
   Pass   1 ♡   Double Redouble
   ?
   What do you bid now?   Your answer_____

6 As South you hold:
   ♠ AKJ10 ♡ AQJxxx ◇ x ♣ Ax
   The bidding has proceeded:

   WEST   NORTH   EAST   SOUTH
   1 ♣   Pass   Pass   2 ♣
   3 ♣   Pass   Pass   ?
   What do you bid now?   Your answer_____

7 As South you hold:
   ♠ KJxxx ♡ 10x ◇ AJx ♣ Qxx
   The bidding has proceeded:

   NORTH   EAST   SOUTH   WEST
   1 ♡   Pass   1 ♠   Pass
   2 ♡   Pass   2 NT   Pass
   3 ◇   Pass   ?
   What do you bid now?   Your answer_____

8 As South you hold:
   ♠ Axx ♡ 10xxx ◇ Jxxx ♣ AQ
   The bidding has proceeded:

   SOUTH   WEST   NORTH   EAST
   Pass   1 ♠   Double Pass
   ?
   What do you bid now?   Your answer_____

9 As South you hold:
   ♠ AQJx ♡ Ax ◇ AK10x ♣ Kxx
   The bidding has proceeded:

   SOUTH   WEST   NORTH   EAST
   1 ◇   Pass   1 ♠   Pass
   ?
   What do you bid now?   Your answer_____

139

10　As West you hold:
　　♠ J　♡ K x　♢ A 10 x x x x　♣ A J x x
　　The bidding has proceeded:

WEST	NORTH	EAST	SOUTH
1 ♢	2 ♢	Pass	2 ♠
Pass	3 ♡	Pass	3 NT
Pass	4 ♠	Double	Pass
Pass	Pass		

　　What is your opening lead?　　Your answer_____

ANSWERS

1　Two Hearts. While there is considerable inducement to try no trump with this particular type of holding, there is no no-trump bid that precisely suits your values. The hand is much too good for a mere rebid of one no trump, which designates a more or less minimum opening, and not good enough for a jump rebid of two no trump, which requires a high-card holding of at least 19 points. A compromise rebid is therefore in order and the suggested one is a raise to two hearts. If partner so much as raises an eyebrow after your rebid, you will go to three no trump. We would have preferred an initial opening of one no trump to resolve this difficulty.

2　Two Spades. A six-card major should be given distinct preference over a four-card minor. With one more club or one less spade, our answer would have been two clubs.

3　Five Spades. Your hand should produce between seven and eight tricks and partner ought to develop between four and five, inasmuch as his bid announces a hand that is equal to an opening bid of one no trump (that is to say, he has between 16 and 18 points). Now it is very true that on a mere point count basis you have not sufficient values for a slam, but distribution operates on your behalf because your singleton and doubleton may render ineffective some of your opponents' high-card strength.

4　Five Spades. Your first response was of a technical nature and merely announced that you had little in the way of high-card strength. Actually you have a hand of great trick-taking power and one with great potentialities. The recommended bid is five spades. A bid of only four spades would be used to describe a hand of no great strength but one in which you prefer spades to no trump. Remember that partner has offered to win nine tricks at no trump even though you have a blank. He, therefore, has all the honor strength and you have the distribution. This makes quite a team.

5 You have sufficient values to insist upon a game contract when partner makes a take-out double. Your hand is above average in strength (11 points), and if partner's double happens to contain exactly the right values, even a slam might be within reach. The best way to announce the strength of your hand is by a bid that is forcing to game—namely, a cue bid of two hearts. This will announce control of the adverse suit and ability to play in any suit that partner selects for trump. Such action is superior to a jump bid to two spades, for this type of jump, after you have previously passed, would not obligate partner to speak again. Take half credit if your bid was two spades.

6 A mere bid of three hearts is the proper call. There is no need for any more violent action than this if you are to assume that your partner knows his way about town. Your cue bid of two clubs was an absolute demand for game, and partner is not permitted to pass at this point regardless of how emaciated a hand he may hold. If he does, then he's the kind of a chap that would drop you in an opening two-bid, and in the words of Webster, "Nothing can be done about it."

7 Three Hearts. Partner's bidding has indicated a holding of six hearts and four diamonds and very likely nothing in clubs to help you stop that suit. You have already shown a good hand and should return to the suit in which the partnership holds eight trumps.

8   Two No Trump. Any hand containing 11 points facing a partner who has made a take-out double offers bright prospects for game and a jump bid is indicated, particularly in view of the previous pass. While normally it is desirable to show a four-card major, a jump to three with a suit this weak is not in accordance with our tastes, where some other suitable bid is available, and our choice is two no trump. Full credit goes to a cue bid of two spades which announces your maximum pass.

9   The forcing rebid of three hearts is our choice. Naturally there should be no question in your mind about reaching game, and slam possibilities are not at all remote. However, you should arrange to make any slam try below the game level and not above. The best bid is therefore a jump in a new suit, preparatory to supporting spades. A jump to four spades would be accepted, but this does not quite do full justice to the hand. One call must be definitely ruled out and that is a jump to only three spades. The reason is that since partner is not the opener, such a raise is not forcing and he might drop it. Furthermore, if after a raise to three spades he proceeds to four, you will be in a position where you must overbid game if you decide to try for slam, and a contract of five might be too high.

10   The Jack of Spades. The bidding has shown that the dummy is void of diamonds. The declarer by his no trump bid indicated that he had some strength in that suit. Your efforts should be directed toward preventing declarer from ruffing diamonds in dummy. Furthermore, no other lead is attractive.

*Your score*_____

DOLPHIN BOOKS

PERSONAL AND PRACTICAL GUIDES

DOLPHIN BOOKS

OF GENERAL INTEREST

DOLPHIN REFERENCE SERIES

DOLPHIN BOOKS

COOKBOOKS

MARRIAGE AND THE FAMILY

DOLPHIN GUIDES

DOLPHIN BOOKS

POETRY AND DRAMA

BROWNING, ELIZABETH BARRETT Sonnets from the Portuguese and Other Poems, C209

CERF, BENNETT, & CARTMELL, VAN H., eds. 24 Favorite One-Act Plays, C423

FITZGERALD, EDWARD, trans. The Rubáiyát of Omar Khayyám, C28

FRANKENBERG, LLOYD, ed. Invitation to Poetry, C24

GILBERT, W. S. *The Mikado* and Five Other Savoy Operas, C158

MARQUIS, DON archy and mehitabel, C26

OMAR KHAYYAM The Rubáiyát of Omar Khayyám, trans. FitzGerald, C28

SHAKESPEARE, WILLIAM Shakespeare's Sonnets, C33

TENNYSON, ALFRED, LORD Idylls of the King, C165

WHITMAN, WALT Leaves of Grass (1855), C3

WILDE, OSCAR The Plays of Oscar Wilde, C137

ESSAYS AND LETTERS

BACON, FRANCIS Essays of Francis Bacon, C67

CREVECOEUR, J. H. ST. JOHN Letters from an American Farmer, C164

DOUGLAS, WILLIAM O. An Almanac of Liberty, C115

LAMB, CHARLES The Essays of Elia *and* The Last Essays of Elia, C6

DOLPHIN BOOKS

HISTORY AND BIOGRAPHY

BALDWIN, HANSON W.   Sea Fights and Shipwrecks, C84

BERNAL, IGNACIO   Mexico Before Cortez: Art, History and Legend, trans.
Barnstone, C422

BURKE, EDMUND   Reflections on the Revolution in France *and* The Rights
of Man, C246
    (EDMUND BURKE: Reflections on the Revolution in France; THOMAS
    PAINE: The Rights of Man)

CATTON, BRUCE   Glory Road, C236

——   Mr. Lincoln's Army, C37

CELLINI, BENVENUTO   Autobiography of Benvenuto Cellini, trans. Symonds,
C129

DANA, RICHARD HENRY   Two Years Before the Mast, C76

DOUGLASS, FREDERICK   Narrative of the Life of Frederick Douglass, an
American Slave, C419

EISENHOWER, DWIGHT D.   Crusade in Europe, C267

FENTON, MILDRED ADAMS & CARROLL LANE   Giants of Geology, C36

GUTHRIE, WOODY   Bound for Glory, C248

GUZMAN, MARTIN LUIS   The Eagle and the Serpent, trans. de Onís, C454

KELLER, HELEN   Teacher: Anne Sullivan Macy, C39

KENNEDY, JOHN F.   Why England Slept, C379

LAVENDER, DAVID   Bent's Fort, C159

MC HENRY, J. PATRICK   A Short History of Mexico, C379

PAINE, THOMAS   Common Sense *and* The Crisis, C49

——   Reflections on the Revolution in France *and* The Rights of Man, C246
    (EDMUND BURKE: Reflections on the Revolution in France; THOMAS
    PAINE: The Rights of Man)

PRATT, FLETCHER   The Battles That Changed History, C38

PRESCOTT, WILLIAM H.   The Conquest of Peru, C166

REITHER, JOSEPH   World History at a Glance (Revised), C406

ROOSEVELT, ELEANOR   This I Remember, C263

——   This Is My Story, C264

ST. JOHN, ROBERT   Tongue of the Prophets, C118

STARKEY, MARION   The Devil in Massachusetts, C308

D 22a

DOLPHIN BOOKS

AMERICAN FICTION

ALCOTT, LOUISA M. Eight Cousins, C324
BEACH, REX The Iron Trail, C459
BELLAMY, EDWARD Looking Backward (2000–1887), C55
BROWN, CHARLES BROCKDEN Wieland, C320
COOPER, JAMES FENIMORE The Deerslayer, C199
—— The Last of the Mohicans, C211
—— The Pathfinder, C173
—— Satanstoe: or, The Littlepage Manuscripts, C176
—— The Spy, C207
CRANE, STEPHEN The Red Badge of Courage, C61
DODGE, MARY MAPES Hans Brinker; or, The Silver Skates, C244
DREISER, THEODORE Sister Carrie, C160
GOLD, HERBERT, ed. Fiction of the Fifties, C299
GUZMAN, MARTIN LUIS The Eagle and the Serpent, trans. de Onís, C454
HARTE, FRANCIS BRET The Luck of Roaring Camp, and Other Sketches, C226
HAWTHORNE, NATHANIEL The Blithedale Romance, C260
—— The House of the Seven Gables, C148
—— The Scarlet Letter, C7
HOWELLS, WILLIAM DEAN The Rise of Silas Lapham, C9
MELVILLE, HERMAN Billy Budd and The Piazza Tales, C307
—— Israel Potter, C296
STOWE, HARRIET BEECHER Uncle Tom's Cabin, C13
TWAIN, MARK The Adventures of Huckleberry Finn, C98
—— The Adventures of Tom Sawyer, C133
—— The Prince and the Pauper, C254
WALLACE, LEW Ben-Hur, C175
WINNERS OF THE LIFE EN ESPANOL LITERARY CONTEST Prize Stories from Latin America, C441

D 19a

DOLPHIN BOOKS

BRITISH FICTION

AUSTEN, JANE Emma, C149
—— Northanger Abbey *and* Persuasion, C34
—— Pride and Prejudice, C74
—— Sense and Sensibility, C174
BRONTE, EMILY Wuthering Heights, C107
BRONTE, CHARLOTTE Jane Eyre, C5
BULWER-LYTTON, EDWARD The Last Days of Pompeii, C277
BUTLER, SAMUEL The Way of All Flesh, C16
DEFOE, DANIEL Moll Flanders, C56
—— Robinson Crusoe, C103
—— Roxana, the Fortunate Mistress, C204
DICKENS, CHARLES A Christmas Carol, C65
—— A Tale of Two Cities, C32
—— Great Expectations, C181
—— Hard Times, C114
—— Oliver Twist, C182
—— The Old Curiosity Shop, C315
ELIOT, GEORGE Silas Marner, C151
—— The Mill on the Floss, C21
HARDY, THOMAS Jude the Obscure, C22
—— Tess of the D'Urbervilles, C138
—— The Mayor of Casterbridge, C153
—— The Return of the Native, C119
—— Under the Greenwood Tree, C333
MEREDITH, GEORGE The Egoist, C223
SCOTT, SIR WALTER Quentin Durward, C89
SHELLEY, MARY Frankenstein, C44
STEVENSON, ROBERT LOUIS Treasure Island, C72
SWIFT, JONATHAN Gulliver's Travels, C86
WELLS, H. G. The War of the Worlds *and* The Time Machine, C304
WILDE, OSCAR The Picture of Dorian Gray, C15
WYNDHAM, JOHN The Day of the Triffids, C130

CONTINENTAL AND OTHER FICTION

FLAUBERT, GUSTAVE Madame Bovary, C19
ORCZY, BARONESS The Scarlet Pimpernel, C269
STENDHAL The Red and the Black, C17
VERNE, JULES Around the World in Eighty Days, C168
—— The Mysterious Island, C292
—— Twenty Thousand Leagues Under the Sea, C167
WYSS, JOHANN The Swiss Family Robinson, C255
ZOLA, EMILE Germinal, trans. Ellis, C297

D 20a

DOLPHIN BOOKS

PHILOSOPHY AND RELIGION

AURELIUS, MARCUS   The Meditations of Marcus Aurelius, trans. Long, C68

BENTHAM, JEREMY, & MILL, JOHN STUART   The Utilitarians, C265
  (BENTHAM: Principles of Morals and Legislation; MILL: On Liberty and Utilitarianism)

BERKELEY, GEORGE; LOCKE, JOHN; & HUME, DAVID   The Empiricists, C109
  (LOCKE: An Essay Concerning Human Understanding (Abridged); BERKELEY: A Treatise Concerning the Principles of Human Knowledge and Three Dialogues; HUME: An Enquiry Concerning Human Understanding and Dialogues Concerning Natural Religion)

DESCARTES, RENE; SPINOZA, BENEDICT DE; & LEIBNIZ, GOTTFRIED WILHELM FREIHERR VON   The Rationalists, C82
  (DESCARTES: Discourse on Method and Meditations; SPINOZA: The Ethics; LEIBNIZ: Discourse on Metaphysics and The Monadology)

FOX, FREDERIC, ed.   A Calendar of Hymns (Magnum), C357

HUME, DAVID; LOCKE, JOHN; & BERKELEY, GEORGE   The Empiricists, C109
  (LOCKE: An Essay Concerning Human Understanding (Abridged); BERKELEY: A Treatise Concerning the Principles of Human Knowledge and Three Dialogues; HUME: An Enquiry Concerning Human Understanding and Dialogues Concerning Natural Religion)

LEIBNIZ, GOTTFRIED WILHELM FREIHERR VON; DESCARTES, RENE; & SPINOZA, BENEDICT DE   The Rationalists, C82
  (DESCARTES: Discourse on Method and Meditations; SPINOZA: The Ethics; LEIBNIZ: Discourse on Metaphysics and The Monadology)

LEWIS, C. S., ed.   George Macdonald: An Anthology, C373

LOCKE, JOHN; BERKELEY, GEORGE; & HUME, DAVID   The Empiricists, C109
  (LOCKE: An Essay Concerning Human Understanding (Abridged); BERKELEY: A Treatise Concerning the Principles of Human Knowledge and Three Dialogues; HUME: An Enquiry Concerning Human Understanding and Dialogues Concerning Natural Religion)

LONG, GEORGE, trans.   The Meditations of Marcus Aurelius, C68

MILL, JOHN STUART, & BENTHAM, JEREMY   The Utilitarians, C265
  (BENTHAM: Principles of Morals and Legislation; MILL: On Liberty and Utilitarianism)

NEILL, STEPHEN, ed.   Twentieth Century Christianity, C426

PLATO   The Republic and Other Works, trans. Jowett, C12

SCHOPENHAUER, ARTHUR   The World As Will and Idea, trans. Haldane & Kemp, C335

SPINOZA, BENEDICT DE; DESCARTES, RENE; & LEIBNIZ, GOTTFRIED WILHELM FREIHERR VON   The Rationalists, C82
  (DESCARTES: Discourse on Method and Meditations; SPINOZA: The Ethics; LEIBNIZ: Discourse on Metaphysics and The Monadology)

THOREAU, HENRY DAVID   Walden, C10